# the Brownie

## Annual 1983

edited by Penny Morris

## THIS ANNUAL BELONGS TO...

# Kentish Town City Farm

**by Penny Morris**

photographs by Mary Vaughan

After arriving, Sarah and Joanne went to see some chickens, in the hen house. The chickens don't seem to mind the extra company, do they?

The goats didn't appear to mind having the Brownies in their pen either, in fact the black one, Minstrel, rather took a fancy to their uniforms and kept trying to eat the buttons and badges!

This pony, Whisper, was pleased to have his mane stroked and stood very quietly for Joanne. There are eleven ponies and horses on the farm, and many local children are members of the Pony Club. Riding classes for disabled people are held every week and the farm now has a small cart specially adapted so that people in wheel-chairs can learn to drive a pony and cart.

If you live in a town or city you have probably never been on a farm. Joanne Leech and Sarah Byrch of the 3rd Kentish Town Brownie Pack hadn't, so they were thrilled when arrangements were made for them to spend a day on a farm. The farm they visited is a very special one as it is a city farm, right on their doorstep in Kentish Town. It is only a small farm, about three acres, and was started in 1973 on some waste land so that local people could have the chance to learn about caring for animals and plants. There are about sixty animals now, plus gardens and a greenhouse. The animals include horses and ponies, goats, sheep, a cow, a pig, ducks and chickens, dogs, donkeys and even ferrets! Joanne and Sarah went along to meet the animals and help with the work.

Visitors to the farm are encouraged to help with the farm work, so Sarah had a go with the yard broom. It looks quite hard work!

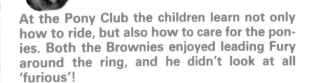

At the Pony Club the children learn not only how to ride, but also how to care for the ponies. Both the Brownies enjoyed leading Fury around the ring, and he didn't look at all 'furious'!

Joanne seemed to get on very well with the ducks. I wonder what they're talking about?

Ermintrude the cow doesn't look very interested in eating the leaf that Joanne is offering her. I think she'd rather eat the grass. She certainly gets on well with the sheep!

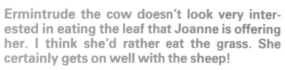

The pig took no notice of the Brownies, preferring to eat her rations. Sarah the Brownie thought it was rather funny that the pig was called Sarah too!

6

Bumble, the donkey, eats hay. The Brownies tried to groom Bumble, but even after they had finished he looked as though he could have done with a haircut!

The puppy, Favour, enjoyed being cuddled by the Brownies as much as they enjoyed cuddling him.

When it was time to say goodbye the Brownies felt quite sad, and I think this horse would have liked them to stay and stroke his nose a bit longer.

There are over thirty city farms in the United Kingdom so perhaps you will be able to visit one. If you are interested in finding out about the one nearest you, write to the City Farm Advisory Service, Inter-Action Trust Ltd, 15 Wilkin Street, London NW5 3NG. And if you do get the chance to visit a city farm, take your wellies, and have fun!

# Your Birthday Flower

## January Snowdrop

*Have you heard the snowdrops ringing
Their bells to themselves?
Smaller and whiter than the singing
Of any fairy elves.*

(from *Snowdrops*
by Sydney Dobell, 1824-1874)

## February Primrose

*A tuft of evening primroses,
O'er which the mind may hover till it dozes.*

(from *I Stood Tiptoe Upon a Little Hill*
by John Keats, 1795-1821)

## March Violet

*There are no flowers grown in the vale,
Kissed by the sun, woo'd by the gale,
None with the dew of the twilight wet,
So sweet as the deep blue Violet.*

(from *The Violet*
by L. E. Landon, 1802-1838)

## April Daisy

*The daisy scatter'd on each mead and down,
A golden tuft within a silver crown.*

(from *Britannia's Pastorals*
by William Browne, 1591-1643)

## May Hawthorn

*The coming of the hawthorn brings on earth
Heaven: all the spring speaks out in one sweet
    word,
And heaven grows gladder, knowing that earth
    has heard.*

(from *The Passing of the Hawthorn*
by Algernon Swinburne, 1837-1909)

## June Honeysuckle

*The honeysuckle sleeping in the oak,
    the flaunting beauty
Revels along upon the wind;*

(from *The Morning Scent of the Flowers*
by William Blake, 1757-1827)

illustrated by Pat Harby

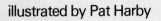

# CATHY'S CHRISTMAS PROBLEM

MUMMY, DADDY, AUNT MARY—SO MANY PRESENTS TO BUY!

ONE EVENING JUST BEFORE CHRISTMAS, THE ROBIN FAMILY WERE SITTING QUIETLY WHEN...

SEE WHO'S AT THE DOOR, PLEASE, CATHY.

I'M COLLECTING FOR THE N.S.P.C.C. WILL YOU HELP?

OF COURSE!

CATHY GAVE THE MAN 50p

MUMMY AND DADDY WERE WATCHING A PROGRAMME ABOUT STARVING CHILDREN.

WE MUST SEND MONEY TO HELP THEM.

HERE'S £1 FROM ME.

I'M GLAD I GAVE TO HELP THE POOR CHILDREN, BUT HOW WILL I BUY CHRISTMAS PRESENTS NOW?

I'LL DO SOME ERRANDS FOR MRS CROFT. IF SHE PAYS ME I'LL HAVE MONEY FOR CHRISTMAS PRESENTS.

COULD YOU GET ME A LOAF, PLEASE?

OH, AND TELL MRS PLATT I CAN'T AFFORD EGGS THIS WEEK.

CATHY'S HEART SANK—HOW COULD MRS CROFT PAY HER?

**by Godfrey Cox**

illustrated by Stanley Houghton

9

WHEN MRS PLATT HEARD ABOUT MRS CROFT SHE GAVE CATHY SIX EGGS TO TAKE TO THE OLD LADY.

EXCUSE THE MESS! I'M MAKING ALL MY CHRISTMAS PRESENTS — IT'S CHEAPER THAN BUYING THEM.

CATHY RUSHED HOME AND TOLD MUMMY OF HER PLAN...

SOON SHE WAS BUSY MAKING CHOCOLATE FUDGE...

...AND MAKING A SHELL-COVERED JEWELLERY BOX.

...AND KNITTING EGG COSIES.

ON CHRISTMAS EVE...

ALL MY PRESENTS ARE READY.

THE FUDGE IS FOR OLD MRS CROFT.

WHY DON'T YOU INVITE MRS CROFT FOR CHRISTMAS LUNCH?

SO MRS CROFT — AND THE ROBINS — HAD A SUPER CHRISTMAS!

# PUZZLE PAGE

## INTEREST BADGE FITWORD

**by Phyllis Mead**

Can you fit the names of the Interest Badges listed below into the spaces on the badge diagram? You will find it quite easy if you count the number of letters in each badge carefully.

```
M       A       A               R
SAFETYINTHEHOME
U   I   T   I   H       O
S   R   I   M   O       O
I   S   S   A   U       K
C   T       L   S       L
I   A     COOK  E       O
A   I       O   O       V
N   D       V   R       E
    E       E   D
    R       R   E
                L
          CRAFT
          C   L
AGILITY     Y
```

**Cook**

**Artist**

**Musician**

**First Aider**

**House Orderly**

**Craft**

**Agility**

**Book Lover**

**Animal Lover**

**Safety in the Home**

## Riddle-Me-Ree

**by Ann Hillyer**

My first is in MAT but not in FLOOR,
My second's in MEADOW but not in MOOR.
My third is in WATER but not in LAKE,
My fourth is in GARDEN but not in RAKE.
My last is in COUNTRY but not in LAND,
My WHOLE is at Brownies, Lending a Hand!

solution on page 61

11

# Prickly Guests

**by Ann Pinder**

illustrated by Chris Sheridan

The hedgehog evolved millions of years ago, so it should know all about the art of survival. Today, though, it has to contend with speeding cars and pesticides which, besides killing insects, also harm insect-eating animals and birds higher up the food chain. Even the creature's habitat has been destroyed where housing estates and motorways have encroached on woodland and hedgerow. We would do well to give a hand to the local hedgehog population, by supplying suitable food and accommodation in pesticide-free gardens, so discouraging them from straying onto busy roads.

One way to do this is to leave a part of the garden overgrown, allowing the leaf litter in the autumn to accumulate there forming a snug bed for hibernating hedgehogs. Sleep takes up a great part of the hedgehog's life, for not only does it hibernate during the winter, it also snoozes throughout the days of summer, unless there is a shower, when, knowing that rain brings out the slugs, it will emerge to gorge itself on them. Otherwise it comes out to feed at dusk, snuffling and snorting along, like the pig or hog after which it is named, turning over leaves and stones in order to find millipedes and worms.

In the vegetable plot are juicy slugs, aphids and caterpillars, and beneath trees fallen fruit. All these are sought for and consumed, as well as the occasional frog, mouse or adder. It might seem a dangerous occupation tackling a poisonous snake, but the hedgehog is well protected by its coat of spines, and by the fact that it is highly resistant to the adder's venom.

A hedgehog's diet is very varied, which simplifies the task of feeding garden visitors. It will eat all sorts of titbits, including chopped bacon rind, cheese, raw minced beef, bread, cakes, chopped orange, strawberries, fruit juices, and, if you are not too squeamish, mealworms.

All hedgehogs seem to like bread and milk, while the occasional raw egg broken into milk will provide much-needed nourishment in the spring, for animals newly woken from hibernation.

During dry periods, too, milk would be appreciated, since then there are few slugs about, but avoid giving milk in a saucer, for this can easily be tipped up. Instead, use a straight sided ceramic dog dish, as this cannot be overturned by the hedgehog putting its foot in the dish, or flipping it over in the hope that, like a stone or rotting log lying on the ground, the best morsels of food will be found underneath.

Sometimes when your prickly guest has found that the dish really does have nothing else to offer, it will push the dish about in irritation. This is a good reason for not putting the dish on a concrete path or patio, unless you want to be woken in the night by the sound of clanking crockery!

Drinking water should be provided, but a garden pond with steep sides can prove a real hazard to small mammals, which fall in when drinking and are unable to climb out up the pond's slippery sides. A pond with shallow, sloping sides will on the other hand prove a real asset. Failing this, sink an upturned dustbin lid into the ground. This will attract birds as well as hedgehogs, so place it in the open to prevent cats from sneaking up under cover of flowers and shrubs.

Hedgehogs like to lie up beneath hedges and bushes, but they also choose woodpiles and refuse, so extra care must be taken when lighting bonfires and breaking up compost heaps, since these may harbour nesting chambers. These are formed by the adult hog pushing into the heap of litter and then turning round and round in order to create a snug hollow, which is afterwards lined with grass and dried leaves.

Young hedgehogs are small, scarcely spiked creatures, blind and deaf at first, and reliant on their mother's milk. After several weeks, though, they may be seen following Mum up the garden path as they go in search of insects.

Usually two broods are born each year, but the youngsters of the second brood, born in late summer, have only a few weeks in which to build up an adequate layer of fat which will enable them to survive hibernation, so they are often not all reared successfully. You could help them to put on weight in autumn by supplying them with a variety of nutritious foods.

You may even like to create a hibernaculum, which will double as a nesting box in spring. Ask Mum or Dad to help you make a special hedgehog house, like the one in the diagram, which was designed by the Henry Doubleday Research Association, at Braintree in Essex. It consists of a box of untreated timber — hedgehogs dislike the smell of wood preservative — entered by a wooden tunnel small enough to prevent cats from getting in and attacking the young. Because the box will be underground when completed, a ventilation pipe is fixed at the back of the box, so that the air is always fresh. To prevent the pipe getting blocked with bedding, the end is wrapped round with chicken wire where it enters the box.

Bury the box beneath a pile of earth or leaves, making sure that the entrance tunnel and the ventilation pipe are kept free of earth. The mound is then covered over with a sheet of polythene to keep everything dry, and this is covered with a layer of earth to make the hedgehog house look as natural as possible.

To attract tenants to this desirable residence, a tasty titbit should be placed at the entrance to the passage, and a pile of leaves or straw left nearby for the hedgehog to use as bedding.

With a snug home and a regular supply of food at its disposal your hedgehog may well decide to take up permanent residence in your garden, giving you an ideal opportunity to observe hedgehog behaviour at first hand. But don't pick up your new pet, or bring it indoors, since that spiky coat harbours a great many fleas and ticks.

Watch how those spikes react when you are near. The hedgehog has some 16,000 spines in all, and when they are lying flat against the creature's body, this indicates that it is not at all frightened, but if the spines on its head and then its body start to stand erect, this

means the hedgehog is becoming alarmed. As a last resort the hedgehog will roll itself into a ball.

A rolled-up hedgehog resembles a sea-urchin which is why the Greek philospher Aristotle named it *echinus*, or urchin. The ancient Greeks often depicted the hedgehog with apples on its back, and even today the animal is said to deliberately impale fruit such as apples and strawberries on its spines, and carry them away to eat later, but whether the fruit is impaled accidentally or deliberately, is open to discussion. Certainly the hedgehog does have some strange habits, like the one of 'anointing', which starts when a hedgehog licks an object like a leaf or a piece of wood, in order to work up a froth in its mouth, which it then smears all over itself. Why it does this we don't really know. Maybe it is a method of grooming, or the animal is disguising its scent, but these are only guesses. Perhaps after you have observed a hedgehog yourself you could come up with some other ideas.

**The H.D.R.A. Hedgehog House**

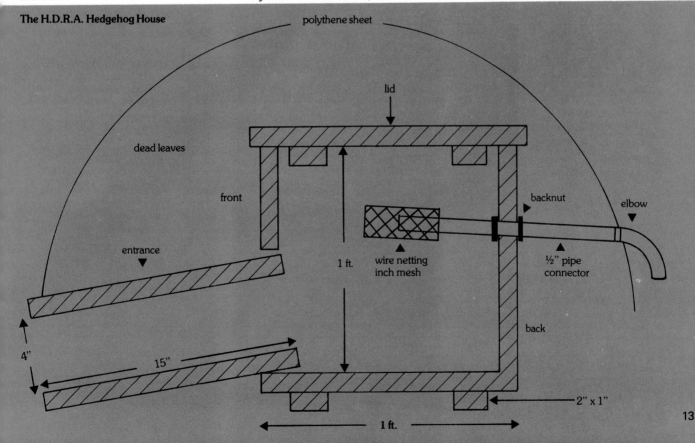

polythene sheet

lid

dead leaves

front

entrance

wire netting inch mesh

1 ft.

backnut

elbow

½" pipe connector

back

4"

15"

2" x 1"

1 ft.

# LET'S BUILD A KITE

**by Ann Martin**

*illustrated by Chris Sheridan*

**Have you ever thought of making a kite? Here's how to make a simple kite that will fly even if there's no wind! You could, if you have room, fly it indoors!**

## YOU WILL NEED

1 polystyrene tile

2 cocktail sticks

2 pieces of string, one 20cm long, the other at least 1m long (longer if you are going to fly it outdoors)

1 elastic band

crepe paper

glue (Copydex or similar)

an old pencil

There are ten stages to making this kite. Make sure you complete each stage before moving on to the next one.

1. Cover your working area with newspaper. Measure your tile to determine the exact centre. An easy way to find the centre of your tile is to place two pieces of string from corner to corner diagonally across the tile. Where they cross is the centre (diagram A).

2. Make a hole in the centre of the tile with one of the cocktail sticks. With the same cocktail stick, make another hole about 7cm above the centre hole (diagram B).

3. Draw a picture or pattern on the front of the tile using felt-tip pens.

4. Thread the 20cm piece of string through the two holes in the tile, securing at the back by tying the ends of the string round the cocktail sticks (diagram C).

5. Attach the elastic band to the bridge of the string, by placing the elastic band over the string and pulling one end of the band through the other end (diagram D).

6. Put the tile on one side while you make the tails. The crepe paper should be rolled up. If it is not, roll it up now. Cut across the roll so that you have about ten strips of crepe paper, each about 2.5cm wide.

7. On the back of the kite, glue a 1cm band along the bottom. Place the ends of the crepe paper strips onto the glued area, keeping the strips close together. Press the strips firmly so that they stick to the tile (diagram E). Put the kite on one side while the glue dries.

8. While you are waiting for the glue to dry, tie one end of your long piece of string to the old pencil. Secure it with a tight knot, then wind the string around the pencil, until only a small piece is free (diagram F).

9. When the glue is completely dry, tie the free end of the string to the elastic band, knotting it tightly.

10. Unroll the crepe paper tails, and you're all ready to fly your kite!
    *REMEMBER** to clear up and put everything away.

The great thing about this kite is that it doesn't need any wind to fly. It is so light that it will fly if you run along and pull it behind you! Try it and see!
If all your Pack makes a kite you could go for a Kite Picnic. Ask Brown Owl about it.

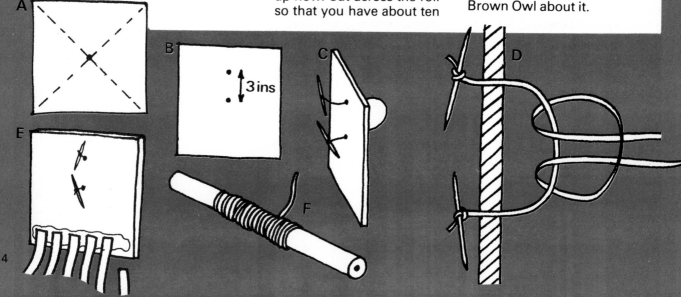

A

B
3 ins

C

D

E

F

# OLAVE BADEN-POWELL

by Tin Forbes

Auriol, elder sister of Olave, with Robert and Katherine Soames, 1906

**Olave St. Clair Soames was born at Stubbing Court, Chesterfield, Derbyshire, on February 22nd 1889. The world was then a very different place from the one we know today. Queen Victoria was still on the throne, and there were no aeroplanes, televisions or cinemas, and very few motor cars. Women would have to wait another twenty-nine years before gaining any kind of vote, and Scouting and Guiding had yet to be invented.**

Olave was the youngest of three children, having a brother, Arthur, and a sister, Auriol. She was called 'St. Clair' after her godmother, and 'Olave' because her father was fond of the Norse sagas and had hoped for a boy he could call 'Olaf'. Like a great many girls of similar background Olave did not go to school—instead she had a succession of nurses and governesses.

Just before her eleventh birthday she began to keep a diary in which she recorded on June 12th 1900: ''Usual Lessons. Begin at 8.00. Auriol practises the piano. I do (on Mondays and Thursdays) History; on Tuesdays and Fridays, Geography; on Wednesdays and Saturdays, Sums, which I positively loathe. Breakfast at 9.00. Walk from 10.00—11.00. Lessons from 11.00—1.00. Lunch. Lessons again from 2.00—4.00. Tea 4.30. Dinner at 7.00. C'est tout. We have a half-holiday every Saturday and do the flowers violently in the schoolroom to look nice for Sunday.''

Olave's father, Harold Soames, was a restless man; consequently he and his family moved frequently from one house to another. By the time Olave was twenty-three they had moved in and out of more than seventeen houses! Some of the houses were amongst the loveliest in the land like Renishaw Hall, home of the Sitwell family, and Cranborne Manor which the Soames family rented from Lord Salisbury, then Prime Minister of Great Britain. All had lovely gardens in which the future Chief Guide learned to love and appreciate the natural world. She had her own dog, her own horse, and at one time she and Auriol ran the 'Cranborne Poultry Farm' which meant that they looked after the hens and chickens, and sold the eggs to their mother.

At the age of twelve and a half her parents decided that her formal education was complete, but of course that did not mean that she stopped learning, simply that she no longer had to do 'book-learning'.

In those days it was not unusual for a girl in Olave's position to stay at home until she was married—indeed, marriage was very often thought of as a girl's 'career'. However, Olave was not entirely happy about this, and at the age of seventeen she secretly wrote off to a hospital to find out about the possibilities of becoming a nurse. The reply was unsatisfactory—she was too young.

So the years went by, happy years in which she was learning all the things that were going to make her such a wonderful Guide. She was keen on all kinds of sport (riding, tennis, sailing, swimming, skating), a lover of animals, interested and concerned about other people, and had a quiet and deep reverence for God. When she was confirmed at the age of fifteen she recorded that now at last she was a Christian 'on her own'. Her young life was filled with activity, and not just activity of a sporting nature. The arts also played their part, especially music. Olave often went to concerts, including the Henry Wood Concerts (The Proms) where she saw the great composer Debussy make his first appearance in England. She herself played the violin, only giving it up when she became busy with Guide and Scout affairs. Her violin 'Diana' she very kindly gave to the Guide Association, as some of you may know. Olave also enjoyed going to the theatre, especially if the famous actor-manager Gerald Du Maurier was playing, for he was her pin-up.

In 1912 Olave and her father went on a cruise to the West Indies. They set sail from Southampton on January 3rd on board *The Arcadian*. It was a voyage which was to change her life, for one of her fellow passengers was a certain Major-General Sir Robert Baden-Powell. They were married on October 30th 1912 when Olave was twenty-three. From now on her life was to be inextricably linked with the Guide and Scout movements, then still in their infancy. Guides everywhere owe a great deal of gratitude to Olave Baden-Powell, the World Chief Guide, who was once Olave St. Clair Soames.

# Try Juggling

## It's Catching!

STAND COMFORTABLY. LOOK STRAIGHT AHEAD. DON'T WATCH ANY ONE THING. KEEP YOUR ELBOWS AT YOUR SIDES. NOTE THAT THE BALLS TRAVEL IN A PLANE PARALLEL TO YOUR BODY. DON'T WORRY ABOUT CATCHING. THE CATCH WILL COME NATURALLY WHEN THE THROW IS RIGHT.

**1**

### ONE BALL - LEARNING SYMMETRY

PUT A BALL IN ONE HAND. THROW IT IN AN ARC - TO EYE LEVEL - TO YOUR OTHER HAND. THROW IT BACK IN EXACTLY THE SAME ARC. PRACTICE THIS THROW IN BOTH DIRECTIONS UNTIL YOU CAN DO IT COMFORTABLY WITHOUT LOOKING AT YOUR HANDS. EVERYTHING YOU THROW FROM NOW ON IS THIS SAME THROW.

**2**

### TWO BALLS - THE EXCHANGE

START WITH ONE BALL IN EACH HAND. THROW THE BALL THAT IS IN THE HAND YOU DON'T WRITE WITH TO EYE LEVEL. THIS IS EXACTLY WHAT YOU DID WITH JUST ONE BALL. WHEN THE BALL REACHES EYE LEVEL AND BEGINS TO DROP...

**3**

...THROW THE SECOND BALL UNDER IT. THIS BALL SHOULD ALSO FOLLOW THE SAME PATH TRACED IN THE ONE-BALL EXERCISE. REMEMBER TO THROW TO EYE LEVEL, KEEP THE BALLS IN THE SAME PLANE, AND DON'T WORRY ABOUT CATCHING. PRACTISE THESE TWO THROWS UNTIL THEY ARE COMFORTABLE AND SYMMETRI-CAL. LEARN TO START WITH EITHER HAND.

**4**

### THREE BALLS - THE FIRST JUG

START WITH TWO BALLS IN THE HAND YOU DON'T WRITE WITH AND ONE IN THE OTHER HAND. THROW THE FIRST BALL TO EYE LEVEL, JUST LIKE YOU DID IN THE ONE BALL EXERCISE. WHEN THE FIRST BALL BEGINS TO DROP...

**5**

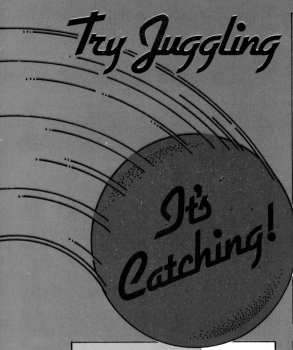

**6**

...THROW THE THIRD BALL UNDER IT. NOTICE THAT, AS IN THE PREVIOUS PANEL, THIS IS THE SAME EXCHANGE YOU LEARNED IN THE TWO-BALL EXERCISE. TO CONTINUE, WHEN THE THIRD BALL BEGINS TO DROP...

**7**

...THROW THE FIRST BALL UNDER IT. THIS SYMMETRICAL PATTERN OF EXCHANGES IS JUGGLING. BY THE WAY, THERE IS NO REASON THE TWO HANDS HAVE TO BELONG TO THE SAME PEOPLE.

**8**

When the four Karamazov Brothers flew in from California to perform their fantastic juggling act on the London stage, they made such an impact on young fans that they decided to start daytime teach-ins at a gymnasium in Covent Garden. They were specially keen to help beginners, and by the end of each session their pupils found they had learned the basic skills and could juggle really well.

To try your hand you'll need three brightly-coloured medium-weight balls which you find easy to catch and hold. The right size will probably be a little smaller than tennis balls. Follow the illustrations and instructions opposite in the correct sequence. You'll need to concentrate really hard to start with — then you'll be teaching your friends how!

photographs by Cecilia Fellner

# SIMPLE SUPPERS

## by Doreen Forni

illustrated by Pauline O'Boyle

### Supper Potatoes

4 medium-sized potatoes
1 tbsp milk
25g/1 oz butter or margarine
salt and pepper
Fillings:
2 rashers of bacon, grilled, then cut into small pieces
50g/2 oz Cheddar cheese, grated
2 eggs
50g/2 oz mushrooms, washed and chopped

1. Light the oven at Gas Regulo 6/400°F/200°C.
2. Scrub the potatoes, then prick with a fork to stop them bursting. Place on a baking tray.
3. Bake in the centre of the oven for 1 - 1½ hours depending on size. They should feel soft when pressed, but also test by inserting a pointed knife or metal skewer to see if they are soft. If still hard leave for a little longer.
4. Take the cooked potatoes out and carefully cut each one in half. Hold with an oven glove. Using a spoon, remove the soft centre of the potato, leaving the skin whole.
5. Mash the potato until smooth, and add the butter or margarine, milk, pinch of salt and dash of pepper.
6. Mix in one or more of the fillings. You could use them all together if you wanted to do a super special supper dish!
7. Spoon the mixture back into the skins, piling it up, then return the potatoes to the oven for about 15 minutes to heat through and brown the tops. Serve hot.

### Macaroni Cheese

75g/3 oz quick cook macaroni
Cheese sauce:
25g/1 oz soft (tub) margarine
25g/1 oz plain flour
½ pint milk
100g/4 oz grated Cheddar or Cheshire cheese
salt and pepper

1. Half fill a large saucepan with water and add 1 level tsp salt. Put on a lid and bring to the boil.
2. Add the macaroni and when the water re-boils turn the heat down and simmer gently for 7 minutes.
3. Drain away the hot water by pouring through a sieve or colander.
4. Leave the macaroni and make the sauce.
5. Put the soft margarine and flour in a small saucepan. Stir together with a wooden spoon and then gently stir in the milk.
6. Put the pan over a low heat and stir very thoroughly with the wooden spoon until the mixture thickens. Always stir right to the bottom of the

pan. Keep the heat low and cook gently for 3 minutes. Stir in half the cheese and allow to melt, then remove from the heat and stir in the macaroni.

7. Pour into a 1½ pint pie dish and sprinkle with the rest of the cheese. Put the dish under the grill and leave until the cheese on top bubbles and goes brown and the dish is heated through. If you have a tomato, slice and decorate the top before grilling. Take care not to burn the cheese. Serve hot with toast triangles.

### Toad-in-the-Hole

100g/4 oz plain flour +
pinch of salt
1 egg, size 3 or 4
½ pt milk
400g/1 lb small pork sausages
25g/1 oz lard or dripping

1. Light oven at Gas Regulo 6/400°F/200°C.
2. Sieve the flour and salt into a mixing bowl.
3. Break the egg into a cup then make a well in the centre of the flour and pour the egg in.

4. Gradually stir the egg, drawing in the flour from round the sides and slowly adding half the milk until all the flour is mixed with the liquid. Use a wooden spoon.

5. Still using the wooden spoon, beat the mixture for 1 minute, then stir in the rest of the milk. The beating introduces air into the mixture, which helps the batter rise.

6. Put the sausages and lard into a roasting tin and place in the oven for 10 minutes, then carefully remove the tin using oven gloves.

7. Pour the batter over the sausages and put back into the oven for 25 - 30 minutes, until the batter is well risen and crisp. Cut into pieces and serve at once.

## Competition Dish

4 eggs, size 1 or 2
1 pt milk
400g/1 lb cooked potatoes
200g/8 oz tomatoes
150g/6 oz Cheshire or Cheddar cheese
salt and pepper

1. Light oven at Gas Regulo 4/350°F/180°C.

2. Butter a 2½ pt pie dish.

3. Break the eggs into a basin and beat with the milk, using a fork.

4. Season with salt and pepper.

5. Slice the potatoes and tomatoes. Grate the cheese.

6. Put a layer of potatoes in the bottom of the pie dish, then a layer of tomatoes, then egg mixture, then cheese. Repeat, using up all the ingredients, finishing with a layer of cheese.

7. Put the dish on a baking tray and cook in the oven for about 40 minutes until the top is golden brown and the egg mixture firm. Garnish with parsley.

## Cheesy Puffs

½ packet instant mashed potato
50g/2 oz butter or margarine
50g/2 oz plain flour
1 egg, size 2, 3 or 4
100g/4 oz Cheddar cheese, grated
salt and pepper

1. Light oven at Gas Regulo 7/425°F/220°C.

2. Prepare the potato following instructions on the packet but use only half the amount of water stated. Mix the butter and flour into the potato with a fork.

3. Break the egg into a basin, then add with the cheese to the potato mixture. Add salt and pepper and mix well.

4. Place the mixture in teaspoonsfuls on a greased baking tray, leaving space between them to rise and puff out. Bake for 15 minutes until golden brown.

5. Serve hot with grilled bacon or bacon rolls. To make bacon rolls, cut rashers in half and flatten with a knife. Roll up and put onto a skewer on a baking tray and cook at the same time as the Cheesy Puffs.

# BROWNIES ROUND THE WORLD

## by Barbara Bennett

# A VISIT TO AMERICA

Betty was having a lovely holiday in America with her Aunty and Uncle who lived in a big town called Jacksonville. The only disappointing thing was that she would miss her Brownie night in her town in England, and Betty was very keen on the Brownies. But her Aunty had thought of that and had arranged for Betty to visit the local Brownie troop while she was in America. It was called Brownie Troop number 502.

Betty was a bit shy at first, but she needn't have been because all the children were so friendly and crowded around to talk to her. They looked fascinated when she spoke and kept saying: "Gee, we do like your accent!" Betty had to listen very carefully to tell what they were saying because, although they spoke English, they pronounced the words differently. Some had names like Brandi, Fran, Arianne and Kari.

The Brownie uniform wasn't a bit like her English one. The children wore beige-coloured tunics with a dainty beige and white striped shirt underneath and a red tie. Some of the Brownies wore beige uniform trousers under their tunics, which Betty thought was a very good idea for the colder weather. Several girls wore a beige sash across their right shoulder with some special badges sewn on, and the troop number. Their hat was a little dark brown skull cap with a Brownie emblem on it.

The Brownies looked very young, and the leader explained to Betty that in America girls are only Brownies from 6 to 8 years of age, and then they join another group and are called Girl Scouts.

At the beginning of the meeting the Stars and Stripes flag of America was put up and the Brownies held a solemn ceremony when they swore an oath of allegiance to the American flag. Then they said their Brownie promise together in front of their own Troop 502 banner. Betty was surprised that they didn't go into sixes, but American Brownies don't have sixes. When Betty told their leader that her leader was called Brown Owl, and that English

Brownies stand in a ring round a toadstool with an owl on it, the leader laughed and said: "Gee, that's quaint!"

The American Brownies sang a song for Betty. It was:

> There's something in my pocket.
> It belongs across my face.
> And I keep it very close to me
> In a most convenient place.
>
> I'm sure you wouldn't guess it
> If you guessed a long, long while.
> So I'll take it out and put it on
> It's a great big BROWNIE SMILE.

And, of course, everyone did the actions of taking a Brownie Smile out of their pockets and putting it across their faces!

Betty taught the American Brownies *her* favourite singing game: *Alice the Camel*. They specially loved the bumping bit!

As it happened to be St. Valentine's Day that very day, the Brownies had brought cards for each other, and one mother had made a cake for each Brownie with a little red heart on top. Everyone had a drink of apple juice, and then Betty gave the leader some packets of jelly babies to hand around. How excited they all were because, believe it or not, they actually don't have jelly babies in America! "What cute candies," they said. (In America 'candies' is the word for sweets.)

After they had eaten, the leader said: "Now, you Brownies, please don't forget your orders for Girl Scout Cookie Week."

"What are you going to cook?" asked Betty.

The leader explained that 'cookies' means biscuits in America, and she told Betty that once a year they hold a Girl Scout Cookie Week all over America in order to make money for the Brownie and Girl Scout funds. The local bakers make different sorts of cookies which they sell at a special cheap price. The Brownies go around getting orders for the cookies from their friends and neighbours. Then they hand in their orders and later on the biscuits are delivered to the people in the most beautifully decorated boxes with pictures of Brownies all round. They are paid for and, after the baker has taken his money, the rest is given to the Brownie funds.

Betty was given a box of mint cookies and a box of peanut cookies to take home to England and share with her own Brownie pack. She said she would keep the attractive boxes for ever.

Now the meeting was coming to an end, so everyone got into a circle and the leader said: "Shall we do the Friendship Squeeze now?"

Every Brownie held hands crossed like we do when we sing *Auld Lang Syne*.

Then one Brownie, who was called Cheri, started the Squeeze. She had to shut her eyes and make a quiet wish to herself, then squeeze her partner's hand, and jump one foot forward (to show that she had had a go). Then gradually all round the Brownie ring each Brownie, and the leader, had a wish and a squeeze. When everyone's right foot was pointing forward, they had all had a go. Betty thought hard

for her wish, and eventually she wished that she would remember all the interesting things she had done on her visit to an American Brownie Pack, when Thinking Day came round.

Then the meeting was over, the leader put away the Stars and Stripes flag and the Brownie Troop banner, and everyone crowded round to say goodbye. Betty went back to her Aunty's house thinking that it was very wonderful that they were all Brownies together, even though they lived in such different parts of the world.

# BROWNIES IN HONG KONG

**Brownies in Hong Kong are very lucky. Because of the hot climate, they are able to do lots of things all year round that Brownies in the U.K. can only do in the summer. One of the most popular badges is the Swimmer badge and it is often the first badge a new Brownie gains.**

Here, two Hong Kong Brownies tell you a little about Brownie Guiding many miles away.

uniforms illustrated by
Kathleen Whapham

## Brownie Thinking Day

On Brownie Thinking Day, every Brownie in Hong Kong went to Yuen Long, a town in the New Territories where our Thinking Day celebrations were to be held. There was quite a lot to see but I thought one of the best things was a display of motorbikes being driven through fires. We had all taken packed lunches which we enjoyed at the show. Later on we all sang lots of songs and one of my favourites was *I've got the B.P. spirit right in my head*. It was a lovely day and we all enjoyed it very much.

*Lynne Griffiths, aged 10.*

## Christmas in Hong Kong

In Hong Kong at Christmas it is hot and sunny, so instead of a Christmas party we had a Christmas picnic. All the Packs in our district went to the playing field at Royal Air Force Sek Kong: we played games, sang songs and had a

competition. Our district is special because all the Brownies' fathers belong to the British Forces. Some belong to the R.A.F. like my daddy, some belong to the Army, but most are Gurkhas from Nepal. We all only stay in Hong Kong for two years and then return to our own countries.

*Lindsay Morris, aged 9.*

# GUIDE DOGS for the BLIND

**by Penny Morris**

Ben works for a teacher, and often leads the way on field studies outings

photographs by Fay Godwin and Norman Redfern

**I expect you have seen and admired the way a guide dog takes a blind person around, crossing roads safely and going into shops and past obstacles. But did you ever stop to think how much training is needed before the dog can do this? And did you realise that the blind person has to be trained too?**

I certainly didn't know how much work was involved until I went to one of the Guide Dogs for the Blind Association's training centres. There are five training centres in Great Britain: Bolton, Forfar, Exeter, Leamington Spa and Wokingham. I went along to Folly Court in

Truffle works in London, leading his owner through busy streets, and even travelling on the Underground!

Wokingham with Gemma Reynolds of the 1st Winnersh Brownie Pack and Lynette Musson of the 1st Embrook Brownie Pack.

The dogs are bred by the Association at a centre in Warwickshire and spend their first year with a puppy walker. The puppy walker house-trains the dog, and gets it used to family life, including being with young children and pets, even cats! The puppy must learn to walk in the middle of the pavement, slightly ahead of the walker, and it must get used to crowds, traffic and shops. The puppy stays with the family until it is about a year old, when it goes to a training centre.

When we arrived at Folly Court we were shown a short film about guide dogs, then one of the trainers brought in Yulie, a labrador retriever. The lecture theatre was quite full, but Yulie didn't seem to mind. Her trainer explained that she was being trained to work with a schoolteacher, so she must get used to being with many people. We were told to clap our hands loudly and make a noise. Yulie didn't even blink!

Then we went to the kennels. The dogs live in large kennels at

Folly Court, generally two or three together, with an outside wired run, and an indoor section where they sleep. We thought it seemed quite luxurious, especially when we were told that the sleeping areas had underfloor heating! Most of the 120 - 150 dogs are between one and two years old and they spend six to eight months at Folly Court.

When the dogs arrive at the training centre they are assessed for their suitability as guide dogs. It is very important that they have the right temperament, and they must also meet the physical requirements, and be intelligent. Most of the dogs at the centre are labrador re-

The Brownies meet some of the dogs in their pens

trievers as they are the most suitable breed, but there were also alsatians and golden retrievers.

The first few weeks at the centre are spent in firmly establishing what the dog has learnt with the puppy walker. The dog must obey commands such as 'sit', 'down', 'come', and 'forward', must always walk in the centre of the pavement and must always sit at the kerb. The dog has to get used to wearing a harness and only when completely at ease in the harness is the dog handed over to a qualified trainer for the most difficult part of the training — teaching the dog to judge heights and widths. It's no good the dog walking under a low obstruction such as a ladder if the blind owner is going to bang his or her head! The dog has to learn to think 'six feet high and three feet wide' so that she and her owner will pass obstacles safely.

The dog also has to learn how to behave in traffic. It must learn that a moving vehicle within a certain area is a signal to stop, even if it means disobeying a command from the blind owner, and that a stationary vehicle is a signal to proceed.

Once the dog has been trained it is matched with a suitable owner. It is essential that the dog and owner are compatible. It would be no good giving a frail old lady a boisterous alsatian, but a younger, active person would need a lively, energetic dog. The waiting time for people wanting guide dogs is about eighteen months but previous owners whose dogs have retired are allowed to jump the queue. Most retiring guide dogs are kept by their owners as pets.

When the dog is ready the blind person comes to Wokingham to be trained. As with the dog, they first have to get used to the harness, walking around with a trainer taking the part of the dog, learning the commands and movements.

Lynette and Gemma meet Yulie after the film

After a couple of days they are introduced to the dog who will be their guide. They have to learn how to look after the dog. They must feed them, groom them, and love them so that the bond is built up between owner and dog. The blind person has to learn to trust the dog as they go out together into difficult situations, in the town, crossing roads and going into shops. It takes about four weeks for the two of them to work perfectly together, and then the blind person pays the Association 50p for the dog and ownership passes to them. It is a basic principle that lack of money should not prevent a blind person owning a guide dog, so sometimes a feeding allowance is given, and the Association pays for a veterinary check-up every six months. The new owner returns home with the dog and at first an instructor visits frequently to see that everything is alright. The Association keeps track of the dogs, visiting them at least once a year. Most dogs work for eight or nine years before they retire.

The object of the Guide Dogs for the Blind Association is to give independence and mobility to all blind people willing and able to train with a guide dog. There are about 2,700 people in Great Britain at the moment with a guide dog, but many more people are waiting for one. The Association receives no state subsidy and relies on the public for funds. It costs £1000 to train a guide dog. Gemma and Lynette were particularly interested in the training of guide dogs as the Brownies and Guides of Berkshire had just raised enough money to sponsor a guide dog. The puppy, who was named Smiley, is going to be trained at Folly Court.

If you would like to know more, write to: The Guide Dogs for the Blind Association, Alexandra House, 9 - 11 Park Street, Windsor, Berkshire SL4 1JR.

Lucy, a two-year-old Labrador

# A DAY IN CAMP

## by Barbara Dunham

photographs by Barbara Dunham and Frank Randall

**Learning how to hammer in a tent peg**

On page 148 of your Brownie Handbook it says, "See if by any chance you can wangle a day in camp". 170 Sixers and Seconds from the West Yorkshire North County Region were lucky enough to attend a special camp day in Bingley. Their hostesses were 80 local Guides and 40 Guiders, all keen to show the Brownies what fun camping can be!

Once everyone had arrived, the Brownies were divided into Patrols with the Guides as instructors, and the first work of the day began. The Brownies were taught how to hammer in tent pegs without hitting their knees, and then they helped to put up the tents.

The next job was to erect the fire shelter, especially as the weather was looking a little threatening. By 11 o'clock the camp site was organised — the tents all pitched and the fires burning merrily.

It was now time for the Colour Ceremony. Three Guides from Bingley unfurled the World Flag, and Miss Cockburn, the County Outdoor Activities Adviser, welcomed everybody to the camp.

Then it was time to start preparing lunch. Each Patrol sent a couple of Brownies to collect the stores — sausages, bread rolls and orange squash. While the stores were fetched some of the other Brownies were shown how to make gadgets. In spite of the problems of square lashing when you only have small hands, the Brownies managed admirably, and before long they had mastered the art of making bedding racks and washing-up stands.

Some of the tents were set up ready for the night so the Brownies could see what it was like to curl up in a sleeping bag on the ground. A few of the Brownies decided they preferred their Pack Holiday camp beds, but many of them thought it was a most exciting way to sleep!

Soon lunch was ready — the sausages were sizzling and the Brownies decided that camping was hungry work. Not a sausage was left!

The afternoon was to be activities time. The Guides had set up various activity centres around the camp site, and the Brownies tried as many as they could. Some of the Brownies made leaf prints, while others followed compass trails. Some made camp prayer books and learnt new graces. In the cook-

**The Guides demonstrate gadget-making**

ing area a group of Brownies were learning the art of making pancakes over an open fire, and were finding it quite tricky. Several of the first attempts were tossed out of the frying pan and into the fire! But soon the Brownies were producing pancakes to be proud of.

At the end of the activities session there was a grand treasure hunt. Miss Cockburn had made up some very strange clues, but the Brownies persisted and eventually one of the Patrols found the 'treasure' and shared it round.

**A washing-up stand in use**

**Learning to make leaf prints**

*Adore Thee* it sounded beautiful as it echoed round the hills.

The day in camp was over and the Brownies all agreed it had been great fun. They had learnt such a lot and were eagerly looking forward to the time when they would be going to Guide camp and could try out their new skills.

Would you like to know more about camp? Why don't you ask your local Guides to come along and show you how to make some gadgets; or perhaps your Pack Leader would tell you some of the secrets of camp? See if you can find the answers to the camp quiz on the next page.

**Cleaning the tent pegs**

It was now time for the Brownies to learn that the way you take down a tent is just as important as the way you put it up. The tent pegs were cleaned and the bedding racks and washing stands dismantled so that everything would be ready for the next camp. The Brownies helped to load up the van and then there was just one more camp activity for the Brownies to enjoy — the camp fire. New songs were enthusiastically learnt and old favourites heartily sung. When the Brownies sang *Father We*

# SECRETS

# OF CAMP

## by Helen Ryan

In Brownies you have lots of secrets, but Guides have secrets too, and many of them are to do with camping. See whether you can find the answers to some of these secrets. When you know the answer draw a ring around the correct illustration.

How do you keep your feet dry when the grass is dewy in the morning?

How do you keep flies off food?

Where does rubbish go?

How do you keep your bedding dry during the day?

How do you keep warm in your sleeping bag?

How do you avoid having soggy soap?

How do you keep dry when you sit on the ground?

How do you keep your clothes clean when you're cooking?

How do you keep your crockery and cutlery together?

How do you keep milk cool in camp?

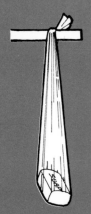

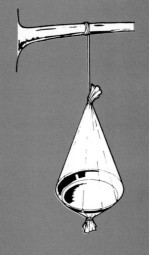

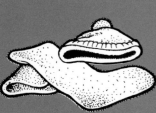

illustrated by Chris Sheridan

# Brownies never give up!

by **Lesley Allan**

illustrated by Moira Maclean

Susan went rushing round the circle of cheering Brownies, her friend Jenny in hot pursuit. She dodged, skidded to a halt, and sat down with a bump in her place, just in time to avoid being caught. She grinned up at Jenny and her friend smiled back.

"You always manage to beat me," she said. "I bet you'll even be able to hobble faster than me when we're little old ladies."

Their Brownie Guider smiled as she heard her. "Never mind, Jenny," she said, "there aren't many Brownies who can beat Susan when it comes to running, and there are many things you can do better than Susan."

The game was brought to a close, and then Mrs Wilton, the Brownie Guider, called the Brownies into Pow-wow, sitting in their circle as they were. "I've got some special news for you," she said.

The Brownies looked up eagerly and with interest. It was clear that something out of the ordinary was coming.

Mrs Wilton looked around the circle. "You all know our District Commissioner, Miss Martin. Well, she has issued a challenge to all the Brownie Packs in the District." She paused for a moment and looked at her excited Pack. "It's a sort of competition. Our Pack is going to work as a team and we shall be competing against all the other Brownie Packs in the District."

The Brownies looked at each other with excitement. Jenny was the first to speak. "What do we have to do?" she asked. "If it's anything to do with sports or games Susan could really help us win."

Mrs Wilton smiled. "I'm afraid all the fast running Susan could do wouldn't help us," she said. "What we have to do is to make a collection and a scrapbook. It must be something of interest to other Brownies."

The Brownies were silent as they thought about this. Mrs Wilton smiled at them all. "Well," she said, "let's hear your suggestions. What do you think we should choose as our subject?"

The Brownies went into their Six corners for a few minutes' discussion, then came back into the Pow-wow circle. One by one the Sixers told of the ideas put forward by their Six, and as they spoke it became clear that most of the Brownies had the same idea.

Mrs Wilton laughed. "Well, it certainly looks as if there is not going to be a lot of argument about the kind of collection we are going to make. Every Six wants to tackle something to do with nature."

"Wouldn't it be a good idea to make a nature collection of things from our own woods and the places near us here at Hillhead?" said Sally, the Second of the Gnomes. "We could show the way nature is round here, and find out all about it."

Everyone liked Sally's idea, so an exciting plan was made. The Brownies would make a trip to the woods to find items for the collection. Everyone in the Pack was thrilled at the thought of this and they all agreed with Susan when she said, "I think we are going to have a wonderful time with this. I *am* glad we're taking part in this Challenge!"

A few weeks later the Hillhead Brownies were to be found out in the woods near home, trying to find interesting items for their nature collection. So many things were collected that they found an ordinary scrapbook was not large enough. Instead the Brownies made an enormous book of their own, out of big sheets of cardboard, which folded up like a concertina.

At last the evening came when the Brownies were able to look at their completed collection. "Do you think we'll win?" asked Susan shyly, putting into words the thought that was in the minds of many of the Brownies.

"Well, I certainly hope so," said Mrs Wilton, looking round the circle at the ring of eager faces turned towards her. "But you know you mustn't be too disappointed if our pack doesn't win. We don't know what the other Packs taking part have done. And whether we win or whether we lose, I'm still very pleased with you. You've certainly done your best, as Brownies should."

"I know we've worked hard and that should be all that matters," said Sally, with a big smile on her face, "but I think it would be wonderful if we *did* win." And all the other Brownies agreed with her.

Two days later Jenny sat on the floor of her bedroom, looking happily at the Pack scrapbook which was spread out in front of her. "Well, I think it's good enough to win," she said to herself, and then laughed as she realised she had spoken aloud. Jenny was very proud that she had been trusted to put the cover on the Pack's scrapbook. Two of the other Brownies had painted the picture for it, but there was nowhere at the Brownie Hall where it could be left for long enough to dry once it had been stuck on, so she had been chosen to take it home to glue.

Slowly and methodically Jenny began to do the job. While she was busy, Ruffy, her energetic little spaniel puppy came squeezing into the room, panting and eager for a game. Ruffy looked at his mistress with great big appealing eyes, but Jenny was firm as she put him outside the bedroom. "I know you don't understand," she said to the little puppy, "but I can't even let you stay in the room while I do this. I hate to think what you would do if you got yourself in among the pages of our collection."

Jenny went downstairs to tea and after she had eaten she went back to look at her handiwork. But when she entered her bedroom a dreadful surprise awaited her. Poor Jenny could hardly believe her eyes. While she had been having her tea Ruffy had managed to get in again. The little dog had been having a fine time while she had been away. He sat in the centre of the floor, contentedly chewing at a twig, the Pack's fine collection scattered in ruins around him.

Jenny looked at the scene and felt the tears well up in her eyes. The weeks of work that the Brownies had spent would all be in vain now. What were they going to do?

At the next Brownie meeting Sally voiced the thoughts of everyone when she said, "I don't suppose Ruffy meant to spoil our chances, but he certainly has." There were tears in Jenny's eyes as she said again and again how sorry she was. Now their nature collection was little more than a heap of scrappy leaves, twigs, torn paper and cardboard.

Mrs Wilton looked around at the faces of her dejected Pack and decided they had felt sorry for themselves for long enough. "Well," she said, looking at them seriously, "no matter how you feel about it, the scrapbook is quite gone. What are you going to do about it?"

"Do about it?" echoed Susan.

"Yes, do about it," repeated Mrs Wilton firmly. "I can see you are upset about what happened, but surely you must have realised by now that the whole point about Brownies is that you don't just sit and worry about things. Brownies set to, and try to put the problem right, whatever it is. If someone needed help, I'm quite certain that you would go and try to help them. Now you are the ones who have had something go wrong, so what do you think you should do about it?"

"Well, we can't enter the competition now," said Jenny, "everything is ruined." She did not add the words 'and it's all because of me' but most of the Brownies could tell what she was thinking by the stricken, guilty look on her face. Many of them were starting to feel quite sorry for Jenny, now they had got over the first shock and disappointment.

"Most of the flowers we collected are past now," said Susan, "so we can't just go out and get some more."

"I don't care." Sally's voice was firm. "We're not going to be beaten!"

The rest of the Pack echoed her determination.

"We must at least try," declared Susan.

"Well then," smiled Mrs Wilton, "if you are going to make an entry of some kind I think you had better put on your thinking caps."

After this the Brownies began to feel a little less glum.

"It's a pity Brownies don't keep ideas in their coat pockets," said Jenny.

Her best friend, Susan, grinned at her. "All I've got in my coat pocket is a handkerchief and a bus ticket." Everyone laughed.

Then Jenny suddenly shouted out, "Yes, that's it, that's it!" and looked excited.

For a moment everyone thought she was mad, and they all started chattering, but Mrs Wilton made the sign for silence.

"Bus tickets could be part of it," Jenny went on, "and coins, and labels off tins and packets and sweets."

"Yes," said Susan, "of course. Everyday things that show what our lives are like day by day."

Suddenly the Brownies were enthusiastic again and Mrs Wilton smiled when she saw the Pack taking heart again and working together once more so that by the end of the meeting it was all planned.

By the closing date for the Challenge competition the new scrapbook was ready. As well as the bus ticket which had led to the idea in the first place, there were library cards, the local newspaper and some comics, some favourite recipes for meals they enjoyed, nursery rhymes for small sisters and brothers, useful telephone numbers, descriptions of people they knew well, an old school notebook, a timetable for the bus, a map of the area, wrappers and labels from the kitchen and many, many more things. Sally had even written down the instructions for favourite games.

The big scrapbook looked marvellous at the Town Hall a few weeks later on display with the other entries for the competition. At last the day for judging arrived. The collections for the District Challenge Shield were to be judged by the Commissioner at Brownie Revels, and the Hillhead Brownies were eagerly waiting to hear how they had fared.

All the Brownies agreed it had been a lovely day. Everything they had done had been centred round the story of Peter Pan. Together they had played one game where they had flown to Never-Never-Land, they had helped Nana the dog look after the children in another activity, they had danced an Indian dance with Rangers disguised as Indians, they had helped the Pirates search for treasure, and played a game in which they helped Captain Hook escape from the crocodile. Last of all they had sung songs with the Lost Boys.

It had been great fun, but now the time had come for the announcement of the competition result. Miss Martin, the Commissioner, was speaking. "My goodness, what a lot of hard work you have all put in. You are all to be congratulated." Someone started clapping and everyone joined in, then Miss Martin continued. "There are five Packs in the District and there are five very good scrapbooks," she said. "Four of the Packs had similar ideas and made nature collections. Only one Pack had a really different idea. The Hillhead Brownies used their scrapbook to tell us about their homes, their schools and their interests and hobbies. A marvellous idea."

Jenny and Susan looked at one another happily. All the Brownies were very excited. "So I have great pleasure in awarding the prize to the Brownies of the Hillhead Pack," concluded Miss Martin.

And there was the prize for them all: a shiny shield with a Brownie badge on it. They passed it round, chattering happily. "Just think," said Susan, "if Jenny's dog hadn't spoiled our first scrapbook, there would have been five nature collections! I wonder if we would have won then!"

"I don't know," answered Jenny.

But before she could go on Susan interrupted. "I know something though; it was your idea about the bus ticket that started it all off. I'll bet there aren't many bus tickets that have won prizes!"

# FROM THE LAND OF THE
# RED DRAGON

### by Jean Phillips
illustrated by Hilary Mullock

As Brownies I expect you know that nearly every country has its legends and beliefs about magical fairy folk or little people. In Scotland there are Kelpies and the Ghillie Dhu, and in Ireland the Leprechauns. Perhaps not so well known are the little people of Wales, the Tylweth Teg. One type of Tylweth Teg are the Bwbachod, the name taken by the Welsh six.

According to legend, the Bwbachod are found around farms, and are usually helpful, but only if treated well. Like all the little people, they can be very mischievous! A farmer at Deunant was told to wall up the door at the front of his house and make a new door at the back. This was so that when dirty water was thrown out it should not fall on the house of the little people! When the farmer did what was asked, his cattle became healthy and he became very prosperous. If the fairy folk were offended they would cause all sorts of mischief and farmers would go to much trouble to try and trick them into leaving.

Fairy folk were believed to sometimes coax children to go away with them. No matter how long the children stayed away, when they came home they always looked and felt as if they had only been away a day or two. Sometimes a fairy would come to live as a mortal. A beautiful lady called Nelfach came out of a lake called Llyn-y-Van in Carmarthenshire, now called Dyfed. She married a farmer, Gwyn, on one condition. Should he ever strike her three times she would return to the lake. They lived very happily and had many sons and daughters, but one day the farmer playfully flicked his wife on the arm with his glove. She turned to him and said, "That is the first causeless blow." A few years later Gwyn tapped her on the shoulder, and she warned him that this was the second causeless blow. He was very afraid then, and for several years was careful, but one day he forgot and lightly touched her on the arm. At this she turned and cried, "Farewell!" then ran to the lake. Gwyn was heartbroken and plunged into the lake after her, but it was too late.

Many months later the lady appeared from the lake again and told her children they would be doctors, and should spend their lives relieving pain and misery. Guided by her, the children learned to collect herbs and make medicines to heal the sick. They later became famous as the physicians of Myddfai.

Fairy folk in Wales are famous for making sweet music and dancing. Sometimes they would give gifts to mortals, but as these gifts were magic they would vanish if wrongly or unkindly used. A fairy harp was given to Tudor ap Rhys, a cottager who lived beside Cader Idris. Everyone who heard the beautiful music felt bound to dance until it stopped, and it gave great pleasure to the cottagers. Then one day a bard, who had said unkind things about Tudor's singing, came to make fun of the harp. Tudor played and played without stopping, and the bard was forced to dance until he collapsed. Then the harp vanished and Tudor ap Rhys never received another gift from the fairies.

Sometimes the fairy folk would help the farmers and cottagers in times of difficulty. During a famine, a little white fairy cow was sent to Corndon Hill, and she stood each morning and evening so that the villagers could milk her. As long as each of them filled only one pail, there was enough milk for everyone and no one starved. But one day a witch,

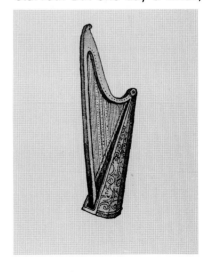

Old Mitchell, decided to put a stop to the supply of milk. She came in the evening with a sieve instead of a pail, and milked and milked until there was no milk left. The cow disappeared and was never seen again, and the witch, for this mean act, was turned to stone. If you go to Corndon Hill you can see her, standing in the middle of a ring of stones known as Mitchell's Fold.

Many strange shapes on mountains in Wales were believed to have been made by giants or dragons. One legend tells of a giant who was on his way to kill the people of Shrewsbury. On the road he met a cobbler, and asked him how much further it was. The cobbler was carrying a sack full of shoes he had collected for mending. Realising the giant was full of evil intentions, he showed him the sack of shoes and said, "I've worn out all these shoes walking from Shrewsbury. You'll never get there by nightfall." The giant decided it was too far away for him to bother and, dumping the sack of rocks and soil he was carrying, he turned and went back to Wales. The huge mound of rocks and earth is still there, and is called the Wrekin!

The fairy folk of Wales were good to those who were kind to them. The good wife of Hafod y Gareg took care of a fairy dog she found hurt. She was rewarded after answering a trick question by having two cows for every one she had previously owned. But be careful if you ask the fairy folk for help! An old woman of Hafod Rugog wanted to break up a large stone that stood by her door, and she also needed half a yard more flannel for a petticoat she was making. She asked the little people to break the first thing she put her hand on at her door, and to lengthen by half a yard the first thing she touched inside the house. When she arrived at her door she slipped and twisted her ankle. She put her hand down to rub it and the bone broke, causing her to fall on her face. As she went into the house she put her hand up to rub her face. At once her nose was half a yard longer!

Another legend explained why Pennard Castle in Gower now lies lost and desolate in the sandhills. Once the castle was a mighty fortress, the stronghold of a great warrior. On the eve of his wedding there was a feast, and music and dancing in the castle. At midnight a sentry looked out from the castle and saw a troop of fairies dancing in the moonlight to the music of many tiny harps. He ran to tell his master what he had seen. The lord of the castle ordered his soldiers to drive the fairies away. One of the guests begged him to leave them, saying, "He who attacks a fairy is forever doomed."

But the lord shrugged this off saying, "I fear neither man nor spirit," and ran among the fairy folk brandishing his sword.

At this a loud voice was heard crying, "He who spoils the fairy dance shall himself be spoiled of all he possesses." The words had scarcely been spoken when a great wind arose and brought with it a cloud of sand. The wind raged all through the night and when day dawned the castle lay buried. The fairies had had their revenge.

Remember, if you meet any of the Tylweth Teg, treat them with respect, and instead of making mischief perhaps they will bring you good fortune!

# HOW!

**by Joan Randall**

'This is one of the best possible ventures you can have'.

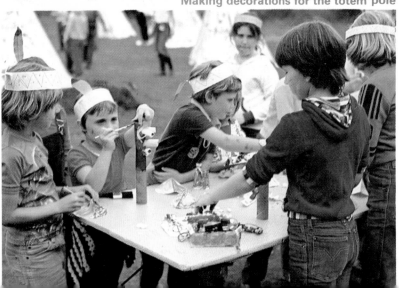

Sign put up for Visitors' Day

Finishing a headband

they decided to be Red Indians when they went to the South West Hertfordshire camp site, Beechwood, for their holiday.

At Pack Meetings beforehand each 'brave-to-be' made and decorated a cardboard headband and cut out and painted a feather to put at the back of it. One of the Tawny Owls gave the long tube from the inside of her new carpet to be a totem pole and a unit helper made a beautiful paper-sculpture owl for the top. When they arrived at Beechwood the Brownies' first job was to decorate their wigwams.

The Brownies put on their old clothes so it wouldn't matter if they got a bit paint-spattered, and painted the

Do you know what this sentence from your Brownie Handbook is referring to? It's talking about a Pack Holiday, and it really is an exciting adventure for those Brownies lucky enough to go away with their Packs.

Usually the Pack chooses a theme for the holiday. The Brownies in the photographs are from the 2nd Bushey Grove and 13th Bushey Packs and

Making decorations for the totem pole

Decorating the totem pole

Admiring the totem pole

names of their tribes — Apache, Comanche, Sioux, and Cheyenne — on their wigwams. The Pack Leaders helped the Brownies to paint their faces, and the Brown Owls and Tawnys were painted too! Egg boxes, cardboard tubes and other waste materials were used to make masks and other objects to be fixed to the totem pole.

Making purses

The war dance!

Enjoying hot prairie dogs

Even Red Indians have to wash up!

Next, the Red Indians made purses, using leather already cut to shape, and wool sewn through the ready-punched holes. Most of them found this rather difficult as there were not enough bone needles to go round . . .

In the afternoon the Brownies played games, and had a camp fire, singing, of course, 'Land of the Silver Birch'!

For tea after the camp fire, the Brownies ate hot prairie dogs with baked beans, cooked by the District Commissioner. While the tea was going down, one of the Pack Leaders took the Brownies on a bear hunt to find tomorrow's supper, but the first spots of rain drove the hunters back, bearless!

All the Brownies and Guiders had a wonderful time being Red Indians — next year they are going to be *pirates*!

HOW!

Comparing the finished purses

**cats**

**cats**

The kittens above
are Jack and Jill,
of *Blue Peter*.

Cats

# BROWNIES or FROWNIES?

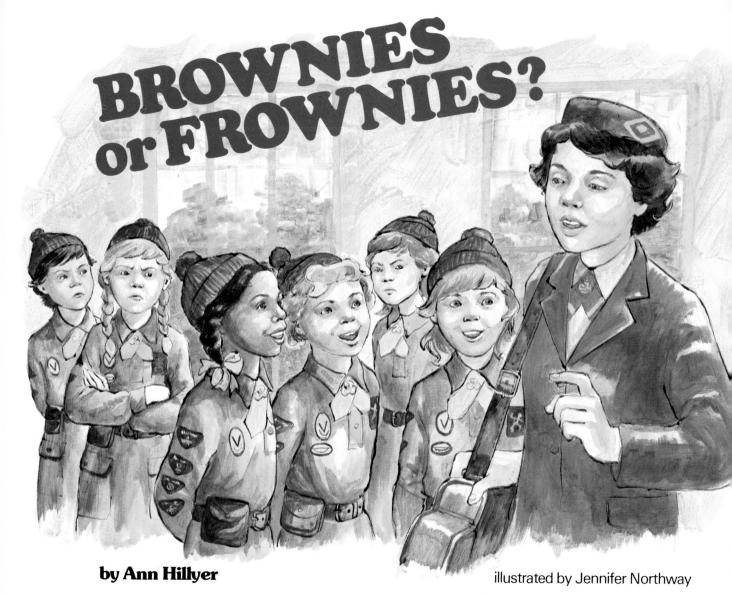

**by Ann Hillyer**

illustrated by Jennifer Northway

"Now, don't forget, next week we shall meet in Motley Wood instead of the Church Hall," Brown Owl reminded her Pack, as they finished their usual Wednesday meeting. "We will make the most of these fine summer evenings, and have a kind of Treasure Hunt."

"Hurray!" "I can't wait!" "That'll be smashing!" cried the girls.

But the Sprites didn't seem very eager.

"I don't fancy going," muttered Vicky, their Sixer.

"I'm too tired after school to go hunting for things," grumbled Jo. And the other Sprites agreed.

It was a happy Pack, except for the Sprites. They were always the last ones to join in, and the first to grumble. The rest of the Pack privately called them "The Sulky Sprites".

Brown Owl had a friendly word with them.

"If you don't enjoy being Brownies, you must leave, and then I can invite some other girls to fill your places," she told them. But they didn't like that, of course!

The following Wednesday evening was warm and sunny. Motley Wood was at its most beautiful. Everyone said how pleasant it was — except the Sulky Sprites.

After some singing and a Pow-Wow, and various lively games, Brown Owl and Tawny handed an empty matchbox to each Sixer.

"Now I'm going to give you twenty minutes to see how many different things you can find to fit in this matchbox," announced Tawny, looking at her watch. "Please don't put in any ladybirds or tiny creatures which like to be free! But you can put in a leaf, a stone, a piece of bark — anything small and interesting. Let's see if you can find fifty things!"

The Elves, the Imps and the Pixies scattered through the wood, laughing and calling to one another as they rummaged around for interesting things. But the Sprites gathered round Vicky, looking miserable.

"I can't see the point of doing all that," said Jo, sulkily.

"Neither can I," added Lisa, frowning.

"Well, let's not bother!" decided Vicky, throwing the matchbox into some bracken. "Come on, let's run off into that thick part of the wood, where Brown Owl won't see us! Then we can tell her we've lost our matchbox — and it will be true, too!"

The Sprites plunged through the undergrowth and found themselves in a shady dell, where the trees were old and twisted.

"It's a bit creepy in here, isn't it?" whispered Tina, the smallest Sprite.

"Nonsense!" retorted Vicky. But a sudden rustling sound from nearby made her jump.

"There's something inside that old hollow tree!" gasped Jo, and before they could run away, out sprang a tiny man, dressed all in brown. He made them a bow and grinned.

"What's that?" the Sprites asked each other.

The little man drew himself up to his full height.

"I'm a Brownie, of course! There are lots of us around, you know. Good deeds, helping hands, smiling faces — that sort of thing. Everyone knows us Brownies. And who, may I ask, are *you*?"

"We're Brownies, too!" said Lisa.

But the little man shook his head. "You aren't," he said solemnly. "It's naughty to tell lies."

"We are!" protested the others. "We truly are Brownies. Look at us!"

Again the little man shook his head.

"You can't be," he told them. "Brownies are happy folk who have lots of fun and say nice things and smile."

"But we do have fun, and we are happy," began Jo, but the Brownie tossed his head.

"I've heard all about you from a friend of mine — a wise old bird who lives in that tall tree back there. She doesn't like people calling themselves Brownies if they aren't. So she asked me to collect you and take you to the Frownies. That's where you belong, I'm afraid."

"The Frownies?" gasped Vicky. "They sound horrible. Let's go home!"

"I'm sorry," said the Brownie, "but orders are orders. Now, line up, please, and follow me. We have to go through the hollow tree down the underground passages into the Gloomy Caverns. That's where the Frownies live — and the best place for them, too!"

The Sprites were so surprised that they followed the Brownie without a murmur.

Into the hollow tree they went, and down a long flight of steps half-hidden by tangled roots. They came at last to a dismal underground corridor.

"Here we are!" smiled the Brownie, rubbing his hands briskly. "The Gloomy Caverns — home of all the Frownies. Come and have a peek at them!"

He opened a door, and the girls peered into a large room. On the floor was the most wonderful assortment of toys they had ever seen. Carved Noah's Arks, stringed puppets, lifelike dolls, musical boxes — and around the toys sat several little people like the Brownie, but with long, gloomy faces.

"Who are they?" whispered Lisa.

"They're the young Frownies!" chuckled the Brownie. "Even with all those marvellous toys, they're still not happy. So now they've forgotten how to play. They never enjoy themselves!"

"How awful!" gasped Tina, and the Brownie closed the door and opened another.

Inside was a magnificent ballroom, hung with crystal chandeliers and garlands of pink and white blossom. Sweet music was playing, and everyone in the room was beautifully dressed. But their faces were frowning and discontented.

"Some older Frownies!" the Brownie told the Sprites. "They're not enjoying this splendid Ball, of course. They never do. They won't join in the dancing either. They're saying that it won't be a very good Ball. Well, of course it won't, if they don't join in!"

He led the girls on to a third room. Inside were a group of grown-up Frownies, sitting on suitcases, just as gloomy as the others had been.

"They look as though they're going on holiday," whispered Vicky.

"They've been!" chortled the Brownie. "They've just been to the most wonderful faraway place, with sandy beaches and mountains and sparkling blue sea for swimming — but they haven't enjoyed it. Frownies never enjoy anything. So now they're sitting there, trying to find something to moan about."

He looked sternly at each of the girls in turn.

"I'd better see if the next room's empty for you," he began, but Vicky gave a gasp of horror.

"Oh no! Please let us go home! We don't want to be Frownies!"

"Well, you've been acting like Frownies," the little man told them.

"We won't any more — we don't want to grow like those horrible miserable Frownies!" Vicky said earnestly.

"All right then," the Brownie decided. "Just one more chance! You know the way back — up those steps and out through the hollow tree. But my wise old friend will be watching you, and if she thinks you are changing back into Frownies again . . ."

The Sprites didn't wait to hear the rest. They scrambled back up the steps as fast as they could, and how lovely it was to escape from the gloom and be back in the sunny green wood again!

"Come on!" Vicky called to her friends. "Let's see if we can find that matchbox — we've got five minutes to fill it! No more Frownies for us!"

And do you know, they kept their word. The others call them the Smiling Sprites nowadays, and they've never had so much fun!

# LET'S MAKE JEWELLERY

**by Ann Martin**

illustrated by Mel Powell

## Bracelets and Necklaces

**There are many methods of making bracelets and necklaces.**

*Using Drinking Straws* Cut up coloured drinking straws into short lengths. Thread lengthways or make a hole with a darning needle and thread crosswise, using coloured wool or strong thread. Try combining lengthway straws with crosswise ones:

*Using Pips* Melon pips are best. Dry your pips completely, then colour them with felt-tip pens or paints. Dry the pips before threading onto coloured wool or strong thread. Try making a pattern using different coloured pips.

*Using Paper* You don't need special paper. Use some scrap pieces — you can colour them yourself with paints, crayons or felt-tips. Cut the paper into triangular shapes. Roll the triangle into a long bead shape, glueing the end to stop it coming undone. Thread the paper beads as for the straws.

## Pendants

Here's how to make a pop star pendant. Put a picture of your favourite pop star on a piece of coloured card. Draw a pencil line .5cm from each side around the picture. Decide on the shape of your pendant: square, triangular, round — any shape you like. Draw the shape you've chosen onto the card, and cut out, but don't cut inside the box you drew first. Rub out the box and turn the card over. Glue the picture to the front of the card and decorate with felt-tips, wool or cutouts. To make the 'chain' for your pendant, attach wool using glue or Sellotape, or punch a hole through the top.

To make an initials pendant, draw and cut out letters in coloured card, and decorate. Then glue to a pendant shape and finish as before.

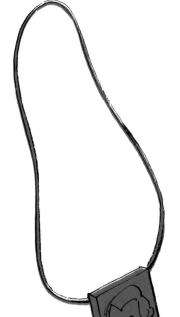

## Brooches

Decide what shape you want your brooch to be, and draw and cut it from coloured card. Decorate with pasta shapes, lentils, sunflower seeds or beads, glueing them in place, or use your initials. Sellotape a safety pin to the back of the brooch.

For a pom-pom brooch, start with the body. Wind some wool around four fingers about forty times. Take it off your fingers and tie lightly in the middle, using matching wool. Cut the loops and fluff out. For the head, wind some wool around three fingers about twenty-five times, and finish as before. Thread a darning needle with some wool and push through each pom-pom four or five times, joining head and body. Add felt eyes, nose and mouth, glueing in place, and sew a safety-pin to the back. Or make a pom-pom pendant, attaching a length of wool to go round your neck.

# Sprout and Cook!

## by Penny Morris

illustrated by Kate Simunek

Imagine a vegetable that you can grow in a few days — which doesn't need soil or sunlight, can be grown at home, will grow all year round, is nutritious and delicious to eat as well! It sounds impossible, but bean sprouts fulfill all these requirements. Why don't you try and grow some?

### YOU WILL NEED

1 large jam jar, or similar glass container (an old, rinsed coffee jar is suitable)

1 elastic band

1 piece of muslin large enough to cover the top of the jar

Some seeds to sprout. You can buy these in most supermarkets and health food shops. Use alfalfa, fenugreek, aduki, lentil or mung bean seeds

### WHAT TO DO

1. Take a dessertspoonful of seeds, put them in a sieve, and rinse thoroughly under running water.
2. Put them in the jar, half fill it with water, then put the muslin over the top and secure with the elastic band.
3. Shake the jar vigorously, then drain the water off through the muslin.
4. Repeat the rinsing process twice more, then put the jar in a safe place.
5. Repeat the rinsing process twice a day, filling the jar half full of water, shaking it, then draining the water off.
6. The beans will be ready to eat in 2 - 3 days, depending on the variety. They are best eaten very fresh. After 6 days they start to get tough, so if you haven't eaten them by then, it is best to throw them away.

### REMEMBER

The seeds do not need heat to grow, so *do not* put the jar on a radiator or anything warm.
Do not rinse the seeds in warm water.
The muslin will get brown as the seed-cases dissolve and wash out.
If the seeds smell unfresh, wash them more frequently.
Discard any seeds that haven't sprouted after 5 days.

There are many ways to use the sprouts. The most common use is in Chinese cookery, but try some other ideas too.

## Sweet and Sour Sprouts

4 cups bean sprouts

1 carrot, peeled and chopped

4 oz/100g mushrooms, washed and quartered

1 small onion, skinned and chopped

1 clove garlic, skinned and chopped

2 cups cooked, chopped chicken

2 tbs/15ml oil for frying

For the sauce:

1 tbs/15g flour

1 tbs/15g sugar

2 tbs/30ml vinegar

2 tbs/30ml soy sauce

Prepare the vegetables before you start to cook. You will need a large frying pan and a spatula to stir the ingredients as they fry. The Chinese use this method for much of their cooking, stir-frying in a large round-bottomed pan called a wok.

1. Mix together the sauce ingredients, stirring so that everything is combined. Put to one side.
2. Gently fry the onion, garlic, carrot and mushroom in the oil. Stir all the time and after about five minutes they should begin to soften.
3. Add the chicken pieces, and continue to cook so that everything is well heated.
4. Add the sprouts.
5. Pour the sauce into the pan, and stir well. Cook for five minutes, then serve with boiled rice.

You could try eating this with chop-sticks!

## Baked Cheese Sandwich

6 slices of brown bread

1 cup grated Cheddar cheese

2 eggs

1 cup sprouts (alfalfa are best)

3 slices of well-grilled bacon, crumbled

½ cup tomato juice

salt and pepper

1. Heat the oven to mark 4/180°C/350°F.
2. Lightly grease a baking tray, then lay the slices of bread on the tray.
3. Sprinkle the tomato juice over the bread.
4. In a mixing bowl, beat together the eggs, cheese, sprouts, salt and pepper.
5. Spread the mixture onto the bread, and put into the oven.
6. Bake the sandwiches for about 15 minutes — they should be puffed up when ready.
7. Serve sprinkled with the bacon pieces.

## Sandwich Spread

1 carrot, peeled and grated

1 cup sprouts (lentil sprouts are good)

4 oz/100g cream cheese, softened in a bowl

salt and pepper

1 tbs/15ml mayonnaise

drop of Tabasco sauce

1. Mix the cream cheese and mayonnaise in a bowl.
2. Add the grated carrot and sprouts, mixing everything together.
3. Add the drop of Tabasco, and salt and pepper to taste.
4. Spread onto brown or wholemeal rolls.

## Green Rice Salad

3 cups cooked rice

½ cup chopped watercress leaves

½ cup chopped parsley

½ cup chopped chives

½ cup sprouts (fenugreek are best)

½ cup French dressing

salt and pepper

1. Put all the ingredients except the French dressing into a large bowl, and mix.
2. Pour on the French dressing, and stir so everything is coated.
3. Chill the salad until you are ready to eat it.

## Cottage Cheese Dip

1 cup cottage cheese

½ cup finely chopped sprouts

¼ cup natural yoghurt

1 clove garlic, crushed

salt and pepper

1. Force the cottage cheese through a sieve into a bowl.
2. Add the yoghurt and mix the two together.
3. Add the other ingredients and mix well.
4. Chill for a couple of hours. Serve with sticks of celery, pieces of raw carrot, or little cheesy biscuits.

# Happy Harry & Gloomy Glum

## by Brenda Morton
illustrated by Chris Sheridan

Sometimes he's Happy Harry, but turn him over and he's Gloomy Glum. Make him for your Toymaker Badge.

Knit him in garter stitch (plain knitting) in double knitting wool, on number 9 (3¾mm) needles.

Happy Harry colours — red, green and pink.
Gloomy Glum colours — dark blue and yellow.

**BODY** Cast on 20 sts in red. Knit 20 rows. Change to blue. Knit another 20 rows. Cast off.

**LEGS** Cast on 20 sts in green. Knit 10 rows. Change to blue. Knit another 10 rows. Cast off. Repeat for second leg.

**ARMS** Cast on 20 sts in green. Knit 6 rows. Change to blue. Knit another 6 rows. Cast off. Repeat for second arm.

**HEAD-HARRY** Cast on 8 sts in pink. Knit 10 rows. Change to green for hat. Knit another 10 rows. Cast off.

**HEAD-GLUM** Cast on 8 sts in yellow. Knit 10 rows. Change to blue for hat. Knit another 10 rows. Cast off.

**To make up:**
1. Fold body in half, dark one side, light the other. Sew sides together at top and bottom (A). Fold an old tights leg and slip into the body. Sew up the opening. Repeat for arms and legs, using less stuffing.
2. Sew legs and arms to body.
3. Stitch eyes and mouths onto the faces — green and red for Harry; red and blue for Glum.
4. Sew the two heads together, leaving the bottom open (B).
5. Use running stitch round the bottom of the face (C) and pull tight. Sew the head to the body, using dark wool, making sure you match the happy face with the bright body. Add buttons, or a loop to hang him from.

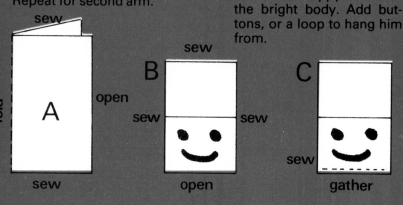

44

# What's in a NAME?

## by Fiona Lawson
illustrated by Debbie Clarke

Have you noticed what odd names some roads have? We found this selection in and around London — yes, they *are* all real! Look around your town for the silliest street name you can find!

**CACTUS WALK**

**ELF ROW**

**ANGEL COURT**

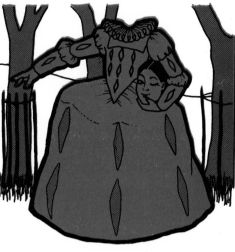

**ANNE BOLEYN'S WALK**

**BEAR ALLEY**

**THE CHASE**

**COLDBATH STREET**

**DOG KENNEL HILL**

**HEN AND CHICKENS COURT**

**HOPPING LANE**

**THE WARDROBE**

**by Penny Morris**

**Have you taken your Book Lover badge?**

**Try this quiz and see how many of the books mentioned you have read. If you get all the questions right you are certainly a book worm!**

1. Anna Sewell wrote a famous book about a horse. What is the book called?
2. In what story do Scrooge and Tiny Tim appear?
3. Who wrote about a phoenix, a carpet, an amulet, a sand fairy, and the Bastables?
4. What is the name of the land where Peter Pan lives?
5. In what book do Toad, Mole and Ratty appear?
6. Who found the *Secret Garden*?
7. Can you name the three literary sisters who lived in Haworth Parsonage?
8. Who wrote the *Just So Stories*?

drawn by Chris Sheridan

9. What is the name of the girl who lived at Green Gables?

10. What is Bilbo Baggins?

11. What is the name of the 'down' in Richard Adams' book about rabbits?

12. What is the title of the book about Meg, Jo, Beth and Amy?

13. Complete this book title: *The Lion, the Witch and the* . . . . . . . .(8).

14. Who or what is Worzel Gummidge?

15. What is the name of the little girl who lives on an alp in Switzerland with her grandfather?

16. Who said, "I'll thcream an' thcream an' thcream till I'm thick!"?

solution on page 61

# A BROWNIE BELL PUZZLE

**by Nina Morgan**

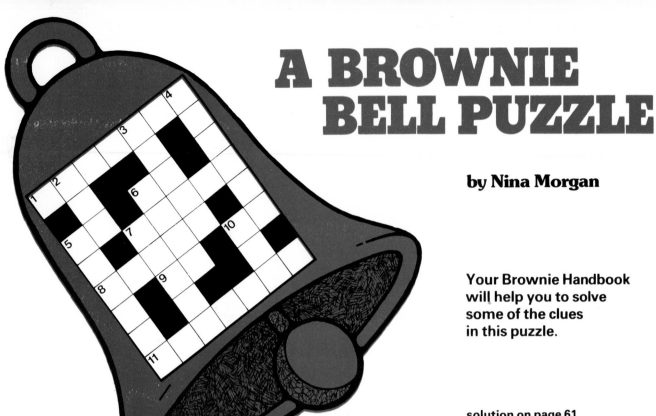

Your Brownie Handbook will help you to solve some of the clues in this puzzle.

solution on page 61

## CLUES ACROSS

1. You could join this six (7)
5. Short for South East (2)
6. "To _ _ or not to be" (booklovers should know this) (2)
7. When you are ten you _ _ _ _ _ Brownies (5)
8. You find me under your vest (5)
9. Busy Brownies are hard _ _ work (2)
10. The third and tenth letters of Challenges (2)
11. These Brownies might like ballet (7)

## CLUES DOWN

2. A tart hidden in Kelpies (3)
3. Pleasant surprise (5)
4. Brownie leaders (6)
5. She helps her 4 down (6)
6. A Brownie promises to do her _ _ _ _ (4)
7. You do this in school *and* at Brownies (5)
10. Blow this into 8 across as part of your First Aid Badge (3)

## A SPRINGTIME OUTING

**by Ann Hillyer**

**TEN** lively Brownies, on a nature trail,
    One stopped to tie her shoe and found a stripey snail.

**NINE** skipping Brownies hurry by the brook,
    One saw some frog-spawn and stopped to take a look.

**EIGHT** laughing Brownies, tramping through the wood,
    One picked up some litter, as all good Brownies should.

**SEVEN** smiling Brownies, striding through the ferns,
    One stroked a caterpillar and everyone took turns.

**SIX** merry Brownies through the meadows run,
    One saw a leaping hare, and followed him for fun.

**FIVE** panting Brownies, jogging down the hill,
    One found a butterfly, and kept very still.

**FOUR** happy Brownies, trotting up the path,
    One watched a sparrow in the dust have a bath.

**THREE** strolling Brownies going up the lane,
    One saw some baby lambs and stopped to look again.

**TWO** tired Brownies, had a little rest,
    One peeped into the hedge and found a blackbird's nest.

**ONE** weary Brownie, no one else in sight —
    But here they come with all their news to tell next Brownie nigh

48

Richmond Park, famous for its deer

# WHITE LODGE – A Very Special School

## by Penny Morris

photographs by Norman Redfern

Every year over 400 young dancers audition for a place at a very special school — the Royal Ballet School, which is housed in a lovely building called White Lodge in Richmond Park, Surrey.

The oldest part of the building dates from 1727, when it was built as a hunting lodge for George I. George II, George III and George IV also spent time there. When Admiral Nelson dined there he drew a plan of the Battle of Trafalgar on the dining table, and that room is still known as the Nelson Room.

In 1955 White Lodge became a ballet school, when the Sadler's Wells Ballet School leased it from the Crown. In 1956 the Queen granted a Royal charter, and it became the Royal Ballet School.

Of the 400 who audition each year, only about one in ten is accepted. Even after passing the audition they must pass a medical, as it is important that they have the right build for ballet, as well as talent.

The pupils, aged eleven to sixteen, follow a normal school syllabus, including CSEs and O levels, as well as receiving ballet training. It is important that they do not neglect their studies, as few will dance with the Royal Ballet as a career. Every year each pupil is assessed, and any who do not reach the required standard, or have physical problems that will affect their dancing, have to leave.

The West Front of White Lodge

First year students in the Front Gallery. The statue is of Dame Margot Fonteyn

49

Swimming is popular

Apart from ballet training, the students enjoy tennis, gym and swimming. The school swimming pool is used for physiotherapy as well as enthusiastic games of water polo! Other forms of dance, country and folk particularly, are also taught. Boys do weightlifting to train them to lift ballerinas. It takes great strength, and must be done gracefully and with apparent ease. Ballet dancers need the energy and stamina of Olympic athletes!

Music is important, too. Most pupils learn an instrument, and singing is popular.

During term most pupils board at the school as they come from all over the country, or from overseas. Their day starts at 8.40 and goes on until 5.45, though general lessons finish at 4.00. Singing practice and rehearsals are held after tea, and homework is done after supper. Pupils attend ballet classes on Saturday morning, too.

Graduates from White Lodge go to the Upper School in Baron's Court, London, when they are sixteen, to continue with their formal education or to train to teach ballet. There they receive their final training before going on to dance with the Royal Ballet or other companies.

In spite of the hard work and discipline, the pupils at White Lodge are grateful for the opportunity to train at the best ballet school in the country.

In biology students learn anatomy and physiology to help them understand how their bodies work

The art room

Pupils relax in their dormitories

of silver in the 19th century and were used for dogs taking part in coursing and dog shows. They were usually finely decorated and engraved, and had a hallmark. The care and detail put into the making of these collars shows how highly dogs were regarded.

# COLLAR THAT DOG!

## by Penny Morris

This German collar is engraved with the date 1809 but was probably made around the year 1700. It is made of brass and iron.

**You could collect many strange and unusual things for your Collector's Badge, but I don't expect you've thought of dog collars! There is a famous collection of over 60 old dog collars in the Dog Museum at Leeds Castle, in Kent.**

This collar, worn by a wire-haired fox terrier, is one of a pair of silver presentation collars made in 1838 for a pair of dogs called Top and Tabinet.

*Perhaps you will be able to visit Leeds Castle and see the collection as Clause 3 of your Collector Badge.*

An Afghan hound is the proud bearer of this French bronze collar dating from 1800.

Dogs have been wearing collars ever since people first befriended them. Paintings and sculptures from Ancient Egypt show dogs wearing collars, and a wall painting in Pompeii dating from before Vesuvius erupted in 79 A.D. shows a dog wearing a collar decorated with metal studs.

In Medieval times dogs were taken hunting on leashes; the Bayeux tapestry has scenes showing hunting dogs. Many hunting collars had fierce iron spikes to protect the neck of the dog against attacks from bears and wolves.

Although most collars had a practical purpose, to restrain and protect the dog, some were worn for decoration and identification. They might be made of leather with brass or copper decorations, or even covered with velvet. Philip II of Spain, who collected dog collars, owned a very fine silver collar decorated with pearls that had originally belonged to the Duke of Burgundy (1342-1404).

The most common type of metal collar, which can still be found today, is the Victorian brass collar. This consists of a simple brass ring with rolled edges to prevent chafing. It fastens with a padlock, and is adjustable so different breeds of dog can wear it. Many of these collars were inscribed with the dog's name and the owner's name and address. There is a collar in the Dog Museum inscribed, 'I am Mr Pratt's Dog, King St, Nr Wokingham, Berks. Whose Dog are You?'

In Victorian times street traders sold dog collars. Prices varied from sixpence (2½p) for the smallest to three shillings (15p) for the larger ones. Padlocks were available to match.

Valuable collars were made

# FOLK FEST 10

## by Penny Morris

Back in 1968, before you Brownies were born, a small group of Scouts and Guides got together to give a concert of folk music for their families and friends. Little did they dream that what started as simple family entertainment would grow and grow until one day it would be a festival of folk music and dance performed by Scouts and Guides from all over the world, before an audience of thousands! I went along to Folk Fest 10 to see how far the festival has progressed since those early days.

The Folk Fest is organised jointly by the Scout and Guide Associations, and starts as a series of workshops held in the spring, where Scouts and Guides audition. The successful entrants then spend the six months before the concert practising and polishing up their acts, helped and encouraged by their leaders and teachers. They are also taught stage craft, how to use a microphone, and even how to apply stage make-up! A production team of professional people involved in broadcasting, entertainment and music get to work to organise the technical side of things. By the day of the performance everything is as professional as anyone could wish.

During the rehearsal I sat at the side of the stalls to watch, while Mary, the photographer, flitted about taking photos. The Royal Albert Hall was bustling with activity as microphones were positioned and lighting patterns worked out. Most of the performers didn't run through their complete act, as they had already rehearsed in the hall several times before. The final rehearsal was to get the technical

These two girls are part of a group called Codicote Folk, formed by 1st Codicote Guides.

Hiroko Ito is a Girl Scout from Kumamoto Troop 3, in Japan. She performed a most beautiful traditional Japanese dance for us.

Here Rolf is seen chatting to the Herefordians. They were the youngest group in the Folk Fest, their average age being thirteen.

This group of singing Scouts are from a small German town called Simmern. They sang traditional German Scouting songs and then finished up with their version of *The Lambeth Walk*, sung in Cockney accents!

photographs by
Mary Vaughan

When the 18th Enfield Ranger Guides and the 14th Southgate Venture Scouts first got together they were just a singing group, but for the last three years they have been dancing together, too.

side, that is the sound and lights, perfect. About halfway through the morning Rolf Harris, who was to be the compere, came bounding onto the stage, and started to chat to the participants, some of whom were beginning to feel a little nervous! After a few reassuring words from Rolf most of them looked much happier. A few problems with the overhead microphone were sorted out, the final act was checked, and then the rehearsal was over.

At 2.25pm the Albert Hall was buzzing with noise as an excited audience sat expectantly in their seats. Guides, Brownies, Scouts and Cubs, plus a large number of friends and relatives of the performers, waited and watched eagerly for the first sign of action on the stage. Then at 2.30 precisely, Rolf appeared. He welcomed us all to the Folk Fest, introduced the first act, and we all settled down to enjoy the show.

These are the 1st Guayaguayare Rangers from the Girl Guides Association of Trinidad and Tobago. As they sang their final song, all the other performers came on to the stage to join in the calypso, waving goodbye.

Malaysian Girl Guides enact part of a traditional Malaysian wedding ceremony.

Shakila Zaman is a Ranger in the Bangladesh Girl Guides Association, who sang traditional songs from her homeland.

55

# Your Birthday Flower

## July   Waterlily

*Floating waterlilies, broad and bright,*
*Which lit the oak that overhung the hedge*
*With moonlight beams of their own watery*
*   light;*

(from *The Question*
by Percy Shelley, 1792-1822)

## August   Poppy

*Pleasures are like poppies spread,*
*You seize the flow'r, its bloom is shed.*

(from *Tam O'Shanter*
by Robert Burns, 1759-1796)

## September   Foxglove

*The foxglove bells, with lolling tongue,*
*Will not reveal what peals were rung*
*In Faery, in Faery,*
*A thousand ages gone.*

(from *Foxgloves*
by Mary Webb)

## October   Michaelmas Daisy

*The Michaelmas Daisy among dead weeds,*
*Blooms for S. Michael's valorous deeds,*
*And seems the last of the flowers that stood,*
*Till the feast of S. Simon and S. Jude.*

(from *A Church Calendar of English Flowers*)

## November   Chrysanthemum

*Lo, from the glowing East*
*Sun-aurioled —*
*Bringing a summer-feast*
*Of bronze and gold*
*Ye come, sweet exiles, to my garden ways,*
*Touching with rainbow light the clouded days.*

(from *Chrysanthemums*
by Edith Jenkinson)

## December   Holly

*The Holly and the Ivy*
*When they are both full grown,*
*Of all the trees that are in the wood*
*The Holly bears the crown.*

(*traditional English carol*)

illustrated by Pat Harby

56

# Around the World with SOUPERKOOK

 Indonesia

by William Dent

57

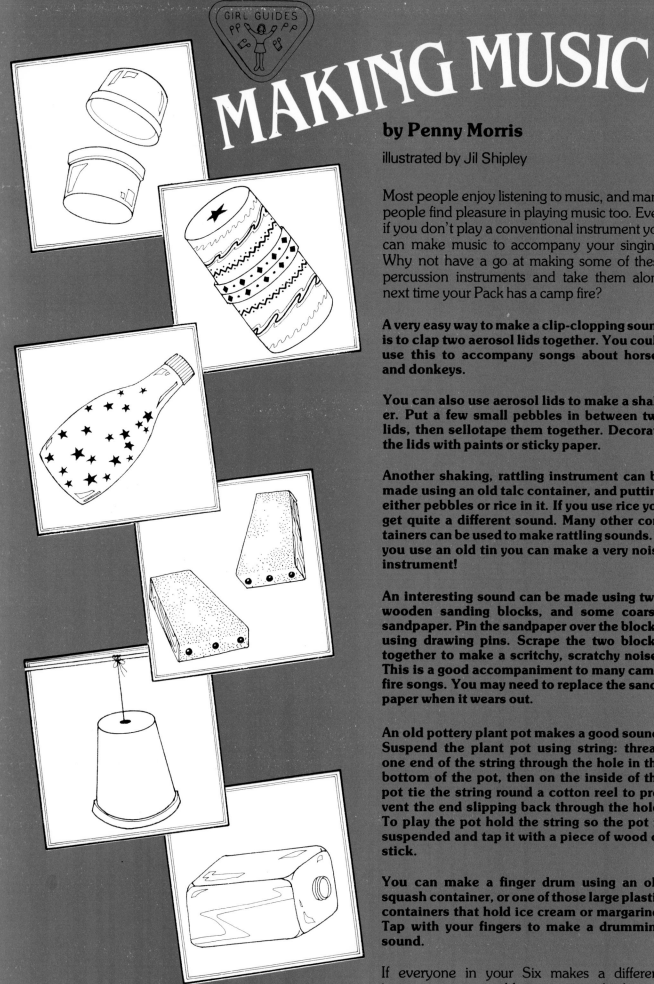

# MAKING MUSIC

## by Penny Morris

illustrated by Jil Shipley

Most people enjoy listening to music, and many people find pleasure in playing music too. Even if you don't play a conventional instrument you can make music to accompany your singing. Why not have a go at making some of these percussion instruments and take them along next time your Pack has a camp fire?

**A very easy way to make a clip-clopping sound is to clap two aerosol lids together. You could use this to accompany songs about horses and donkeys.**

**You can also use aerosol lids to make a shaker. Put a few small pebbles in between two lids, then sellotape them together. Decorate the lids with paints or sticky paper.**

**Another shaking, rattling instrument can be made using an old talc container, and putting either pebbles or rice in it. If you use rice you get quite a different sound. Many other containers can be used to make rattling sounds. If you use an old tin you can make a very noisy instrument!**

**An interesting sound can be made using two wooden sanding blocks, and some coarse sandpaper. Pin the sandpaper over the blocks using drawing pins. Scrape the two blocks together to make a scritchy, scratchy noise. This is a good accompaniment to many camp fire songs. You may need to replace the sandpaper when it wears out.**

**An old pottery plant pot makes a good sound. Suspend the plant pot using string: thread one end of the string through the hole in the bottom of the pot, then on the inside of the pot tie the string round a cotton reel to prevent the end slipping back through the hole. To play the pot hold the string so the pot is suspended and tap it with a piece of wood or stick.**

**You can make a finger drum using an old squash container, or one of those large plastic containers that hold ice cream or margarine. Tap with your fingers to make a drumming sound.**

If everyone in your Six makes a different instrument you could give quite a lively performance at your next camp fire!

# SOUND EFFECTS

## by Penny Morris

If you are not very musical, and don't feel you could do justice to the instruments on the previous page, perhaps you should try sound effects? Sound effects on radio programmes are very sophisticated nowadays, but there was a time when there were a limited number of sounds that could be reproduced in a studio. During the 1950s Spike Milligan was working on a programme called *The Goon Show* and he wanted to use unusual sound effects. According to Spike the only sounds the Variety Department had available were 'a knock at the door', and 'tramps on gravel'. Spike was eventually successful in introducing the use of strange effects. The Drama Department had more resources available to them, and Spike took advantage of these. The following are some of the sound effects Spike used in one show: clock type mechanism, whoosh, double whoosh, wild hammering, crash with knives and forks, footsteps down 9 flights of stairs, pouring liquid, continuous, spasmodic snoring.

There are difficulties in using sound effects realistically. An effect clumsily handled or badly timed can ruin the atmosphere of a play. Drama studios usually have an 'effects' door, with a knocker, bell, and locks. You would think it an easy matter for the character to knock and the door to open and shut. But if the timing is wrong it can sound as if the character went through the door before it opened!

Making sound effects can be great fun and is quite easy:

CORK POPPER This is easy to make. Use either a pop gun, or an old bicycle pump with the end removed and a cork pushed in the end. Follow this noise with the sound of pouring water.

SEA SOUND Put dried peas in a large sieve and swish them around to make the sound of the sea.

THUNDER To make this sound use a thunder sheet, a piece of metal sheet hung up and hit so that it rumbles. Or drum on the side of a metal tank or filing cabinet.

FOOTSTEPS Make the sound of footsteps on gravel using a shallow tray filled with sand or gravel.

HORSES Clap together two empty coconut shell halves, or two walnuts, to make the sound of horses trotting along a road.

BIRD SONG Wet the end of a cork, and rub it against a pane of glass, to make a sound like a bird chirping.

Don't forget that one of the most useful instruments is your own voice! Experiment (preferably when alone!) and find out what sounds you can make. Try being a train, a clip-clopping horse, a car, farm animals, and wild animals. See what noises your friends can make and put them together into a sketch. Record yourselves and play the sketch to your Pack. For a party game, get the listeners to write down what they think the different noises are meant to be.

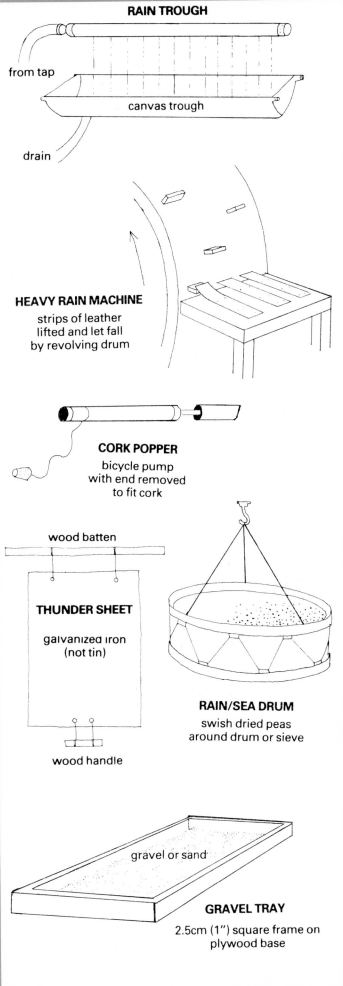

**RAIN TROUGH**

from tap

canvas trough

drain

**HEAVY RAIN MACHINE**
strips of leather
lifted and let fall
by revolving drum

**CORK POPPER**
bicycle pump
with end removed
to fit cork

wood batten

**THUNDER SHEET**

galvanized iron
(not tin)

wood handle

**RAIN/SEA DRUM**
swish dried peas
around drum or sieve

gravel or sand

**GRAVEL TRAY**
2.5cm (1") square frame on
plywood base

# WIN A VISIT TO MR KIPLING'S BAKERY!

Brownies — why don't you enter our competition and try and win a trip to see Mr Kipling cakes being made?

All you have to do to enter is think of an appropriate and imaginative name for the recipe on page 19 entitled COMPETITION DISH. If you were serving this to the rest of your Six as a supper dish, what would you call it?

When you have thought of a suitable name, write it on a postcard with your name, address, age and the name of your Brownie Pack. I would also like you to tell me what you liked best in this Annual, and why. This is very important as it helps me to know what you would like to see in the next Annual.

Send your entries to: The Editor, The Brownie Annual, 17 - 19 Buckingham Palace Road, London SW1W 0PT.

The closing date for entries is March 31st, 1983.

Winners will be notified by post, and the Editor's decision is final.

# STUCK FOR A CUP?

by Nina Morgan

If you've ever forgotten your picnic cup, you'll be glad to know a quick and easy method to make one. Practise at home first. You'll need a stiffish piece of paper, about 20cm square — a shiny brown paper bag or greaseproof sandwich bag would do.

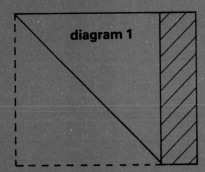

**diagram 1**

1. If your paper is not square, fold it as shown in diagram 1 and tear off the extra slip. Fold the square in half to make a triangle.

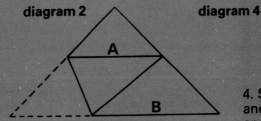

**diagram 2**

2. Lie the triangle down with the folded edge at the bottom. Pick up the left hand corner and fold across as shown. The edge marked A should be parallel to the folded edge B.

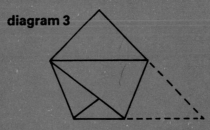

**diagram 3**

3. Do the same with the right hand corner.

**diagram 4**

4. Separate the flaps at the top and fold one down to the front, and the other down the back. Open it up and you have an ideal picnic cup.

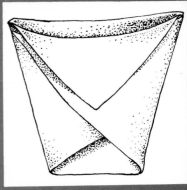

If you use a piece of paper about 50cm square you can make a paper hat.

# ANSWERS

**INTEREST BADGE FITWORD**

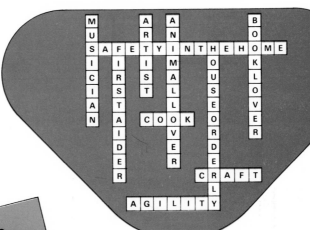

**Riddle-Me-Ree**

Tawny

**ARE YOU A BOOK WORM?**
1. *Black Beauty*; 2. *A Christmas Carol* by Charles Dickens; 3. E. Nesbit; 4. Never-Never Land; 5. *The Wind in the Willows* by Kenneth Grahame; 6. Mary Lennox; 7. Emily, Anne and Charlotte Bronte; 8. Rudyard Kipling; 9. Anne; 10. A Hobbit; 11. *Watership Down*; 12. *Little Women* by Louisa M. Alcott; 13. Wardrobe; 14. A scarecrow; 15. Heidi; 16. Violet Elizabeth Bott.

**A BROWNIE BELL PUZZLE**

**ACROSS**
1. Sprites
5. S.E.
6. Be
7. Leave
8. Chest
9. At
10. As
11. Dancers

**DOWN**
2. Pie
3. Treat
4. Sixers
5. Second
6. Best
7. Learn
10. Air

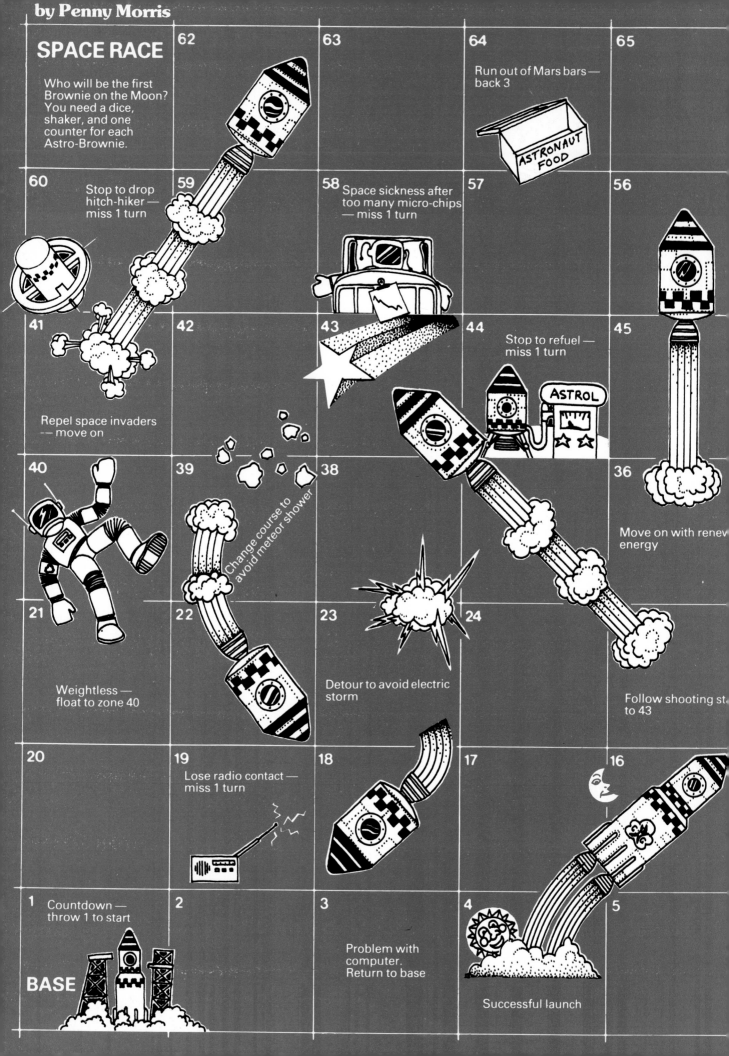